Ding Dong Mine

A History

Peter Joseph & Gerald Williams

Published by The Trevithick Society
for the study of Cornish industrial archaeology and history

The Cornish Mine logo is the Trade Mark™ of the Trevithick Society

The Trevithick Society is a Registered Charity, No. 246586

ISBN 978-0-9575660-3-3

Printed and bound by

Booths Print, Penryn, Cornwall TR10 8AA

Typeset by Peninsula Projects
c/o PO Box 62, Camborne, Cornwall TR14 7ZN

Aerial photograph of the western part of the mine showing the Greenburrow engine house, bottom left. Lode back workings on Bussa Lode extend from bottom left into the distance while workings on Bossiliack Lode extend from near the centre of the view right towards the engine house. The Newlyn River runs right to left in the background, where more shallow workings can be seen. *Bryan Earl.*

Foreword

In 1984 Gerald Williams submitted to the *Journal of the Trevithick Society* an article on Giew Mine. In the thirty years since, he has contributed articles on the history of some twenty west Cornwall mines. In 1996 he wrote an article on the early history of Ding Dong Mine, followed the next year with one on the mine in the nineteenth century. Few writers on Cornish mining history have covered so many mines in such detail as has Gerald Williams. His long fascination with Ding Dong Mine has resulted in this present volume.

Peter Joseph, a trained geologist and industrial archaeologist, began his contributions to the *Journal of the Trevithick Society*, in 1996, with a study of the archaeology of Botallack Mine, revealed by recent fires which had destroyed the dense vegetation there. Peter followed that piece with a series of articles on mines along the cliffs of St Just and Morvah parishes. Subsequently, he has written articles on subjects as diverse as Durfold China Clay Works, the archaeological remains of mining in the Cot Valley, St Just and on the Trevithick Society's collection of artefacts, collected over several decades. He has also written short histories of several other west Cornwall mines. His books include *Hard Graft: Botallack Mine in the Twentieth Century* (2010) and *Mining Accidents in the St Just District* (1999). He has also edited several books on mining as well as up-dating and editing *Cornish Engineering* (Holman Brothers), originally written by the late Clive Carter and *Levant: A Champion Cornish Mine*, by the late John Corin. He was recently made a Fellow of the Royal Historical Society, a prestigious and deserved recognition.

Peter's collaboration with Gerald in this project has resulted in a book on Cornish mining history, which I believe will be enjoyed by all those interested in the subject. Their efforts have resulted in a fine book about a wonderful old mine.

Allen Buckley. September 2013.

Authors' Foreword

Research on Ding Dong Mine commenced in 1996 when Gerald published the first of two articles in the Journal of the Trevithick Society; the second appeared in 1997. It was not long after that that Allen Buckley, then Editor of the Journal, suggested that a larger study of the mine – covering its entire history – would be of interest. Following protracted research a first draft of the history appeared in 2004. After this Peter became involved and it was decided to restructure the work and carry out more research, the result of this being the present publication.

Ding Dong Mine is such a widely known mine although almost nothing had been written about it before Gerald's article of 1996. Even now, little more than a few paragraphs can be found on the web regarding what is usually described (inaccurately) as Cornwall's oldest mine. Many myths have been invented and repeated and this book hopes to dispel these. Both authors are pleased to have produced such a complete history of this iconic mine and its satellites.

Acknowledgements
Thanks go to Nick Johnson for use of Cornwall Historic Environment Services photos and to Tony Clarke and Doug Luxford for photos from their collections. All other photos are from Gerald Williams and Peter Joseph and all line drawings are by Peter Joseph. Thanks also go to Allen Buckley, Tony Brookes and Brian Jones for comments on previous manuscripts and to Graham Thorne for proof reading the present one.

Contents

Chapter 1

Introduction

Ding Dong Mine is one of the most widely known tin mines in Cornwall and, traditionally, regarded as one of the oldest. Despite the mine's prominent standing, very little is known regarding its history, although research suggests that the reason for this is a distinct paucity of records. Standing on the windswept Penwith Moors, the isolated and bleak setting has fascinated tourist and Cornishman alike. Three engine-houses still stand: the Greenburrow pumping house in the western section of the mine dominates the landscape for miles and is often incorrectly referred to as "Ding Dong Mine" (or even "Greenburrow Mine", which never existed), the original workings as Ding Dong lying 700 yards east-north-east of Greenburrow.

The history of the mine covers four periods. Firstly its origins, of which very little documentary or physical evidence exists, followed by the gradual merging of numerous small-scale workings from which the two principal mines, Ding Dong and Wheal Malkin, evolved. The third period – the greater part of the 19th century – saw the mine emerge as an important tin producer in West Cornwall and, finally, the various and ultimately unsuccessful attempts to re-work the mine in the twentieth century.

Many apocryphal stories survive concerning the antiquity of the mine. Indeed, Ding Dong's origins have been the subject of myths and suppositions of almost Arthurian proportions and, attractive as these may be, many are, in reality, utter nonsense. In many cases it seems that a variant of Murphy's Law has been followed (*sufficient research will always support one's hypothesis*) rather than to look dispassionately at what real evidence is available and arrive at a logical conclusion. Other traditional accounts one may like to believe

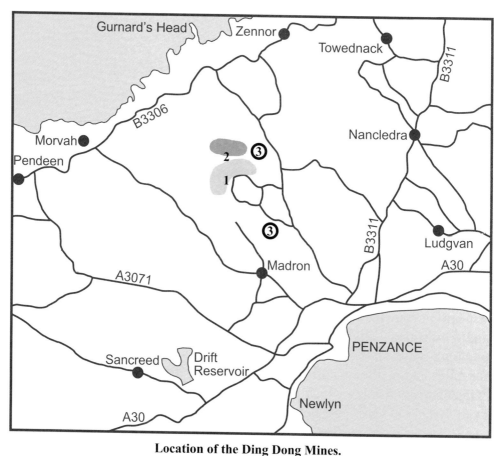

Location of the Ding Dong Mines.
1: Ding Dong; 2: North Ding Dong (approx.); 3: East Ding Dong/Mulfra Hill;
4: South Ding Dong

but historical dating renders them equally incongruous. One was that Christ visited the mine with Joseph of Arimathea, the latter being a skilful sailor and navigator as well as a wealthy trader and merchant. If such were the case, which cannot be disproved,[1] it is certain that if there were a tin working in existence at that time, it would not have been known as Ding Dong.

It is also said that Ding Dong was the mine from which the copper was raised to make the brass for Solomon's temple, but two facts render this story highly improbable. In the first place Solomon died around the year 932BC (which would have made Ding Dong a very old mine indeed!), and the second point is that at no period in its history was Ding Dong ever reported as being a copper producer. Other revelations take a more humorous turn. Writing in the Spring 1950 issue of the *Cornish Review*, Charles Marriott, a former art critic of *The Times*, records that he had been assured by an ancient man at Ding Dong that: "This was the mine from which tin was raised to make the saucepan out of which our Saviour had his bread-and-milk".[2]

There is a further amusing anecdote concerning the age of the mine. In *Cornwall and its People* by A. K. Hamilton Jenkin, the author relates an incident in which he was shown a 'Cornish penny' by an aged miner which had recently come into the latter's possession. The coin was in fact a locally minted token bearing the inscription "Dolcoath Mine, 1812". The old man remarked that it was a "braa ould coin", sure enough, and further stated that there was only one mine in Cornwall older than Dolcoath. "And that's Ding Dong", declared the old man, "which was worked before the time of Jesus Christ, so I reckon that theer penny's close upon two thousand years old". Then with the air of conceding a great favour, he added: "but I'll sell it to 'ee for fifty pounds if you've a mind to".

Even in more recent times unfounded comments regarding the mine's origins have been made. In 1972 a mining text book stated:

> The Romans probably started the first hard-rock mining in a mine which later came to be called the Ding Dong Mine.[3]

Unfortunately, the internet is a splendid means of spreading these myths and untruths. Many websites contain expressions such as "one of the oldest mines in Cornwall" and even "... Ding Dong copper mine, which is one of the oldest mines in the world); the list seems almost endless and if the contents of this book can make any alteration to these preconceptions remains to be seen. A somewhat different story appeared in March 2010, which said that "It is said by the locals that Ding Dong is so deep that at the bottom on a Sunday morning you can hear the Church Bells in Australia !!!!!".[4] This rather interesting myth, whatever its origins, is easily dispelled not least because none of the shafts at Ding Dong approach anywhere near Australia.

Amusing (and sometimes frustrating) as these stories are, they and many less amusing stories, stemming mainly from the pens of 19th century romantics, embellishing legend and tradition to suit their own concepts of history, have only succeeded in distorting history and then creating more confusion, The purpose of this study is to lay such ghosts to rest and adhere to what is known to be true.

Chapter 1 references

1. The date of this visit would be about 64AD, this apparently erroneous date being due to the fact that many Hebrew names were titular, and that the persons then owning those names were not the people normally associated with them.

2. Notes per John Corin.

3. Martens, Charles D. (ed), 1972. *Underground Mining*, Volume 1. Joy Manufacturing Company,

4. March 2010 Newsletter of the Cornish Association of South Australia Inc. p5, article by Tom and Libby Luke.

Chapter 2

Why Ding Dong?

"To the tintinnabulation that so musically wells
From the bells............From the rhyming and the chiming of bells."
Edgar Allan Poe 1809-1849

"Why was the mine called Ding Dong?" This question, so frequently asked, has never been resolved for one simple reason – no one knows. Many theories have been propounded as being likely explanations, but none has succeeded in firmly establishing the origin of the name.

Does the name necessarily indicate a campanological association? Many believe that it does and that the mine derived its name from the bell which rang to signal the changing of cores or shifts. This bell is now housed in Madron church. So, was the mine named because of the ringing of a bell? Possibly, but it would not have been in any way unique as the ringing of a bell to indicate change of core was common practice. Therefore Ding Dong was not outstanding in that respect, indeed the name was not confined to this one mine, although the 19th century family of Ding Dongs in West Penwith – East Ding Dong, (formerly known as Mulfra Hill Mine), North Ding Dong (precise location uncertain), South Ding Dong (about half a mile to the SSW, near Bosworthen) and West Ding Dong (about three miles away in the parish of Sancreed) all owe their existence to the success (or at least the perceived success) of Ding Dong itself. On the coast to the south of St Just there is also a Carn Ding Dong; while there are mines nearby none share the name.

The name, moreover, was not confined to Cornwall. In Hatchwood, on the

Devon side of the Tamar and one mile north-east of Gunnislake, there still stands a small head frame on Dyers Shaft of Ding Dong Mine. At some time in the last century Ding Dong was part of the group of mines known as Bedford Consols, but in 1809 it was a separate concern. During the two wars the mine had been reworked, in the last war for tungsten.[1] There were other mines in Cornwall with a 'ring' to them, namely Ting Tang in the parish of Gwennap, and Retanna Hill Mine in Wendron parish was locally known as 'Bal Ding'.

On the Furness Peninsula there was yet another Ding Dong. This was a nickname for the Number 45 Pit, Lindal Moor Iron Mines, some four miles north of Barrow in Furness, and originated in the 1920s when a group of children would cross a plank spanning the old shaft and discharge volleys of stones. The echo of the stones bouncing off the walls of the shaft prompted the children to call it Ding Dong, and to the present day the name has remained.[2] Looking farther afield there are mines called Ding Dong in Australia, the United States and South Africa.

Was Ding Dong a corruption of another Cornish name or dialect word? Possibly this is true, many Cornish words were still in use at that time although the language itself had fallen into disuse, but a corruption of what? One theory was that the original name was 'Dindods', and that a mine of that name was at work in the West Country in the reign of Henry III (1216-72). The same sources stated that Dindods originated from the words 'din' which supposedly was the Cornish for high ground, as in Castle-an-Dinas, and 'dods' was said to be a rendering of 'daws', meaning dance, (no doubt associated with the nearby circle known as the Nine Maidens[3] or 'Dancing Stones').[4]

Rather perversely, the first 1-inch to the mile Ordnance Survey map of 1801 shows Ding Dong as 'Ting Tang', while Wheal Malkin is 'Wheal Walgang'. This is surely a case of difficult to read writing, but does show how easily variations of names can be produced. Bottrell suggests that the name was Din-a-doyng "if I remember rightly" "and other ancient workings known as Wheal Malkin, which are now united to Ding-Dong, were wrought by the Jews in the time of King John".[5] Unfortunately this reasoning is unsound in that 'din' does not mean 'high ground', but 'hill fort', and 'dods' can scarcely be deemed a rendering of 'daws'. Indeed the latter does not indicate a stone circle unless it is preceded by the Cornish word 'Meyn' (also spelled maen, both ironically pronounced 'mine') as in 'Meyn an Dons' (The Dancing Stones),[6] Last, but not least, the major flaw in this argument is that the Dindods Mine referred to was not in Cornwall, but Devon, and that it was said to have been at work not in the time of Henry III, but in the reign of King John.[7,8]

It has also been suggested that Ding Dong means 'the head of the lode', which if so would imply an outcrop of tin ore in the area, and that the early tinners found it there on surface and had only to dig down into it.[9] As the earliest mining operations in the area would, without a doubt, have developed from streaming operations, where the streamers would have followed tin uphill towards its source, followed by outcrop workings (some of the best outcrop workings in Cornwall can be seen here), this is quite possible.

Another theory that may possibly be near the mark is that the name stemmed from a secondary meaning of the English 'ding dong', meaning 'in good earnest', or with a will as used in the phrase "to go to it ding dong". If this is the case the mine's name would then fall into the list of propitious names such as Wheal Providence, Wheal Fortune, Wheal Prosper etc, intended to signify that the venture would be a success.[10] Also in local dialect we speak of "givin' 'un bell tink", again meaning to do something vigorously or energetically. Another spurious origin is that the mine was named after the Ding Dong bell in Madron parish church, the complete opposite of reality in that the bell came from the mine.

However, the origins of so many mine names have been lost in the mists of time, and it is by no means unlikely that Ding Dong has shared the same fate.

Chapter 2 references

1. Booker, F. *The Industrial Archaeology of the Tamar Valley*, p139
2. Wickenden, M., 1984. The Ding Dong. *The Mine Explorer*, Volume 1, , pp77-87
3. The name 'maiden', so often associated with Cornish stone circles, may originate from the Cornish word 'meydn', meaning stone (information from Craig Weatherhill)
4. *The Cornishman* 7.2.1957, article by Mr Charles Hoare of Penzance Old Cornwall Society
5. Per Oliver Padel, letter to Gerald Williams, August 4th 1988

6. Bottrell, W., 1880. Stories and Folk Lore of West Cornwall. F. Rodda, Penzance

7. Henry de la Beche, *Report on the Geology of Cornwall, Devon and West Somerset*, 1839, p648. HMSO, London.

8. Collins, J. H., 1912. *Observations on the West of England Mining Region*, p469. Royal Geological Society of Cornwall.

9. Jennings, Canon Henry, 1936. *Historical Notes on Madron, Morvah and Penzance*, p12. Saundry, Penzance.

10. Per Oliver Padel, *op. cit.*

Chapter 3

Setting the Scene: A Description of Ding Dong Mine

Ding Dong is unusual in that the mine, along with its satellites, lies between the two nearest mining 'districts' (St Just and St Ives), separated from both by stretches of un-mineralised ground. Ding Dong's only near neighbours are Garden or Morvah Hill Mine, situated near the summit of Watchcroft, to the north, and Carn Galver Mine, about half-a-mile NNE of the former. Both mines were formerly worked as a joint venture under the name of Morvah and Zennor United Mines prior to 1840, in which year the mines ceased and the materials were advertised for sale.

Compared with the mines around St Just and St Ives however, Ding Dong is in a state of almost total isolation. It is situated on a stretch of moorland between the high ground to the north (including Watchcroft and Carn Galver) and an escarpment bordering lower ground to the south-east which opens to Mounts Bay. Mulfra Hill lies to the east, on the west side of the Try Valley, while the ground slopes gently to the west and south to the Penzance-Morvah road. There are no villages nearby and certainly none on the moor; majority of miners would have walked several miles to and from work, in the winter a dreary walk to a dreary place. To quote J. Harris Stone from a work published thirty years after the mine's closure:

> But of all the dismal, doleful places I have ever seen, Ding Dong Mine is *facile princeps* (easily the first). It is reached by the vilest of rough roads, and stands a pitiable ruin, weirdly depressing in the midst of a desolate picture.[1]

One of the most unfortunate aspects of this isolation is that, despite the fame and prominence of the mine, no contemporary photographs are known, although this is sadly true of so many other Cornish mines.

The western part of the mine is dominated by the Greenburrow engine house standing on its burrow, around which are many lines of old shafts and lodeback workings. The Grade II listed house is a prominent landscape feature for miles around, standing at a height of about 200m above sea level. It lies atop an old waste tip with sheer drops to the west and north used by off-road enthusiasts. In places the ground to the north is flat and comprises a prairie-like grassland which in places grades into heath and in others to bog. To the north of Greenburrow lie the Nine Maidens stone circle and the Men-an-Tol, both important Neolithic structures, while to the south farmland has both encroached on to the moor and been lost to it.

The western part of the mine; aerial view showing the Greenburrow engine house (far right) and lines of lode-back workings, mostly on Bussa Lode, from bottom right to top left. Workings on Bossiliack Lode run parallel with the footpath just south of the engine house. The outlines of old field systems can also be seen, much overgrown. Clymo's Shaft is the prominent feature in the centre. *Cornwall Historic Environment Services.*

View of Ding Dong from the east showing all three engine houses: Greenburrow in rear, Ishmael's just below it and Tredinnick to the left. *Tony Clarke.*

To the north and west of Greenburrow the land drops away from the engine house to a comparatively flat moor, broken by lines of outcrop workings, shafts and waste tips. The numerous footpaths are becoming narrow holloways through constant erosion by walkers and more recent damage by off-ride cyclists and motorcyclists. The Newlyn River lies about 750m north of the engine house, a Becher's Brook about 2m deep, parallel with which is a run of small shafts which run to the south-west for at least 700m. A possible streamworks can be seen at the south-western end. Openworks run west from just south of the engine house, and long runs of shafts and outcrop workings run SSW-NNE to the west. East of the engine house are the large mounds surrounding Bolitho Shaft, while farther east can be seen Highburrow Shaft.

Almost due east of Greenburrow Shaft is an area of the mine which was greatly disturbed during the early 20th century operations to rework the dumps. This includes the Jacobine section and a number of shafts, notably Wheal Jacobine. The origins of this name are not known. Jacobins were supporters of the French Revolution; thus it is possible that the name may

23

have come about between the end of the 18th century and the earliest part of the 19th.

The central part of the sett has now been partly reclaimed by the moorland and partly by farmland. The dry, dressing floors and the four engine houses which formerly lay there have had their stonework recycled and little can now be seen of them. The dressing floors are covered by dense, almost impenetrable, vegetation while the remains of the old winding engine house, if any exist, are presumed to lie in the vegetation on the south side of the footpath just east of the stamps. This section is on a south-easterly slope, the path constrained by Cornish hedges, and feels quite different to the open moor, only 200m away.

Further east is a number of shafts, including Killiow Engine Shaft and Ding Dong Engine Shaft. At the eastern end of this run is Ishmael's whim engine house with the huge loading for its winding drum loading, just north of the hamlet of Boskednan.

To the north of Ishmael's whim lie Ding Dong Cottages, a row of three terraced houses. Ishmael's Shaft itself is a prominent feature, a hillock partly

The possibly Bronze Age Men-an-Tol with the Greenburow engine house on the horizon. Men-an-Tol means 'holed stone' in Cornish.

protected by a wire fence, just west of the engine house. The Tredinnick pumping engine house lies downhill to the east, next to the road to New Mill, and is almost invisible on the hillside, being surrounded by trees and partly covered by ivy. Just what Elisha Marks and his band of masons would think if they knew that their constructions were still standing 150 years after the mine's closure can only be conjectured, despite the current poor condition of the buildings.

A number of shafts were formerly in use to the north and south of this area but most have now been capped. This is an area of narrow lanes bordered by Cornish hedges, a great contrast to the rest of the mine. Mulfra Hill Mine or East Ding Dong lies on the eastern edge of the moorland immediately south of Mulfra Hill. The moor has reclaimed the mine and little can now be seen apart from a few shafts and a possible reservoir. The engine house, what little remains of it, are hidden beneath dense vegetation. Farther south, just east of Trythall, the site of South Ding Dong has been completely given over to farmland.

Chapter 3 references

1. Stone, J. Harris, 1912. *England's Riviera. A topographical and archaeological description of Land's End, Cornwall, and adjacent spots of beauty and interest.* K. Paul, Trench, Trubner & Co., Ltd., London.

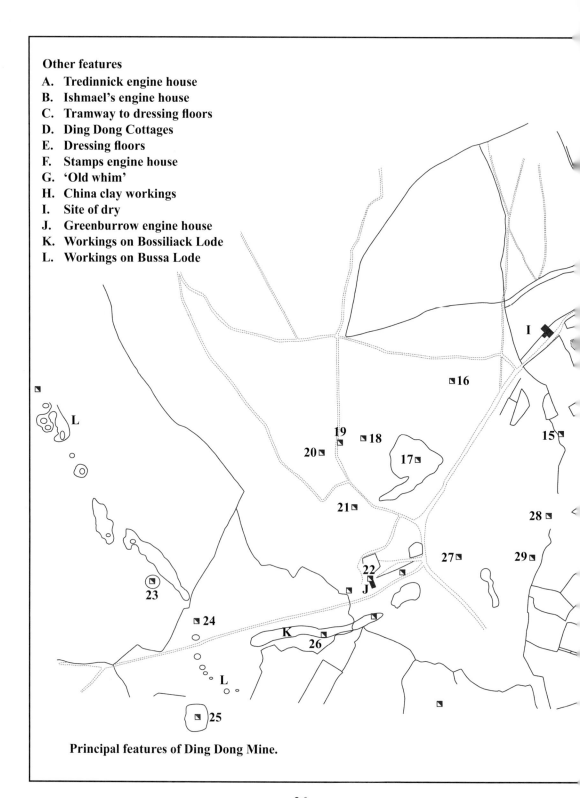

Other features

A. Tredinnick engine house
B. Ishmael's engine house
C. Tramway to dressing floors
D. Ding Dong Cottages
E. Dressing floors
F. Stamps engine house
G. 'Old whim'
H. China clay workings
I. Site of dry
J. Greenburrow engine house
K. Workings on Bossiliack Lode
L. Workings on Bussa Lode

Principal features of Ding Dong Mine.

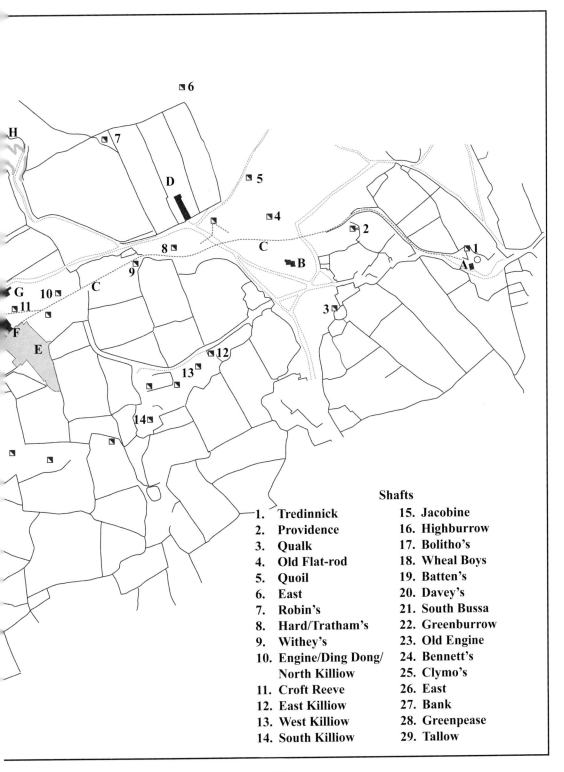

Shafts

1.	Tredinnick	15.	Jacobine
2.	Providence	16.	Highburrow
3.	Qualk	17.	Bolitho's
4.	Old Flat-rod	18.	Wheal Boys
5.	Quoil	19.	Batten's
6.	East	20.	Davey's
7.	Robin's	21.	South Bussa
8.	Hard/Tratham's	22.	Greenburrow
9.	Withey's	23.	Old Engine
10.	Engine/Ding Dong/	24.	Bennett's
	North Killiow	25.	Clymo's
11.	Croft Reeve	26.	East
12.	East Killiow	27.	Bank
13.	West Killiow	28.	Greenpease
14.	South Killiow	29.	Tallow

Chapter 4

Setting the Scene 2: The Geology of Ding Dong Mine

Although the geology of this mine is outwardly very simple, a series of tin lodes in granite, in detail it is very complicated and no sensible, detailed, description has so far been written. The science of mining geology unfortunately only came about in the 20th century; before this it was the miners and the mine agents who were the experts on mineral deposits. The Lands End granite is just one of several outcrops of a single mass which extends from Dartmoor to Scilly and beyond. It is an igneous rock formed by the melting of other rocks and was intruded into the surrounding rocks as a hot, plastic, mass which cooled and crystallised. The intrusion of the Lands End granite took place during the late Permian-early Carboniferous times and has been dated at about 270 million years although this is probably incorrect and is most likely 15-20 million years older.[1] The granite is known as an "abundantly megacrystic" type, which means it contains more than 10% of feldspar crystals longer than 15mm.

After the granite had solidified a series of hot, salt waters (called brines), passed through it and caused it to fracture. It was the presence of radioactive elements such as uranium and thorium in the granite which produced sufficient heat to generate convection (so-called "hydrothermal convective cells") in the pore water in the rocks adjacent to the granite. The circulating fluids removed metals from the adjacent rocks; the 'hydraulic fractures' were places where the metals (moving as salts in the brines) were deposited and are called lodes; the passage of these brines was frequently repeated a number of times, causing repeated phases of mineralisation.

In the Ding Dong area the lodes comprise quartz veins associated with jasper

The principal features of a hydrothermal convective cell.

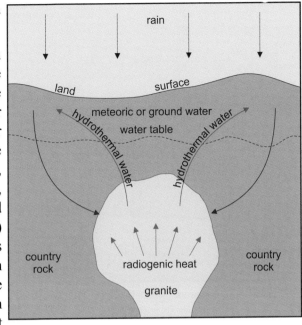

(a mixture of quartz and iron oxide) and capel[2] which are associated with cassiterite (tin oxide) although in other parts of Cornwall a number of different metals were deposited, including copper, tungsten, lead, silver, antimony, uranium and iron. Both native (metallic) copper and copper sulphides occur in the mine although in very small quantities. The minerals tend to occur in the altered granite adjacent to the quartz vein although the cassiterite may also be associated with tourmaline, a black mineral usually seen as thin veins within and about the lode. The quartz itself, while giving an indication of the presence of the lode, tends to be barren.

Where these fractures are not mineralised they are usually referred to by geologists as faults. Cornish lodes tend to be normal faults as opposed to reverse faults, the difference being that the area above the normal fault is dropped relative to the observer whereas in reverse faults the area above the fault is raised (see figure overleaf). The stepped nature of the fractures means that the steeper parts of the normal faults become mineralised. The lodes tend to dip steeply, usually around 70 degrees. Where the dipping lode is seen the upper side is known as the hanging wall (because it hangs when the lode has been removed) and the bottom side as the foot wall (which is walked on after the lode has been removed).

The general trend of Cornish lodes is NE-SW. This trend was caused by the direction of horizontal stresses in the earth's crust when the lodes were formed (during the Variscan orogeny, broadly from 390 to 310 million years ago); the stresses were orientated NW-SE and the lodes formed at right angles to

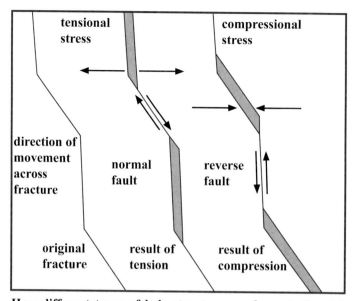

tensional stress

compressional stress

direction of movement across fracture

normal fault

reverse fault

original fracture

result of tension

result of compression

How different types of lode structure are formed. Cornish lodes are formed through tension.

this direction, where horizontal stresses were lowest. There are notable exceptions to this trend, however, and lodes running almost at a right-angle to this trend are known, the best-known being the St Just mining district. Also, in most other areas the ore deposits occur where the lodes are in the vicinity of the granite contact with the overlying rocks (known locally as 'killas'); the Ding Dong deposits were apparently formed at some distance inside the granite rather than at its periphery. At Ding Dong several lode trends are present: NNE-SSW, NNW-SSE, E-W and NE-SW.[3] The different trends were almost certainly formed at different times, however there are no descriptions of lode intersections at the mine and, consequently, no means of dating them relative to each other except by reference to the mine plans, an unsatisfactory method at best.

Over twenty lodes are known at the mine but all worked to different depths and extents. None of the lodes was worked to any great depth and it is likely that the tin mineralisation dies out not far below the bottom of the mine. A report on the mine,[4] undated but probably written in the latter part of the nineteenth century, divided the structures into four categories; these are similar to those of Dines[5] but are based on the author's personal knowledge of the mine rather than inspection of the plans. These were:

1. Standard Lodes
2. South East Lodes
3. Caunter Lodes
4. North and South (Cross) Lodes

Other structures include crosscourses and slides, none of which carry tin but which may cut off oreshoots in any of the other structures. The Standard Lodes were the most important structures in the mine. They trend roughly east-west and dip steeply north and comprised quartz, capel and decomposed granite in about equal quantities with irregular veins of jasper. Nine standard lodes were worked, the most important being Bossilliack, Malkin and Ding Dong Standard. Malkin Lode was the most important and was productive over a 400 fathom length in the western part of the mine and 100 fathoms in the east. Ding Dong Standard carried a rich deposit of tin 330 fathoms in length and 30 fathoms in depth, "having in section the appearance of an archer's bow with the string undermost".

The South East lodes trend from 6 to 26 degrees south-east and north-west and dip south at angles of 75 to 85 degrees. Their composition is similar to that of the Standards. Six of these lodes have been worked in different parts of the mine, with varying results, from White Lode in the south to Robin's Lode in the north. The White Lode yielded large quantities of tin from its junction with Malkin Lode on the west, to a cross-lode on its east over a length of 110 fathoms and depth 20 fathoms. Robin's Lode was found very productive from the Great Cross Course in the centre of the mine, apparently its western extremity, to Cross Lode on the east, a length of 200 fathoms with a depth of 25 fathoms. Both White and Robin's Lodes are connected with large patches of elvan. In some places the elvans were very feldspathic and fine grained and looked like sandstone; at other points they were very hard and quartz-rich. Other lodes are Hugh's, Sut Bal, Jilbert's and Ishmael's

The Caunter lodes vary from 20 to 60 degrees north-east and south-west, averaging 45 degrees. They all underlie north-west from nearly vertical to 85 degrees. There are many of these lodes which were found to be very small, in many cases being only a minute quartz vein or a tiny plate of decomposed granite. In very rich deposits, as on Jacobine, Providence, Rowe's and other lodes, two or more veins were found sometimes several feet apart with numerous small veins branching from one to the other. Bunches of tin were worked on eleven of these lodes with an average depth of 20 fathoms and a total length of 700 fathoms. Those with the most easterly bearing were found to carry most tin.

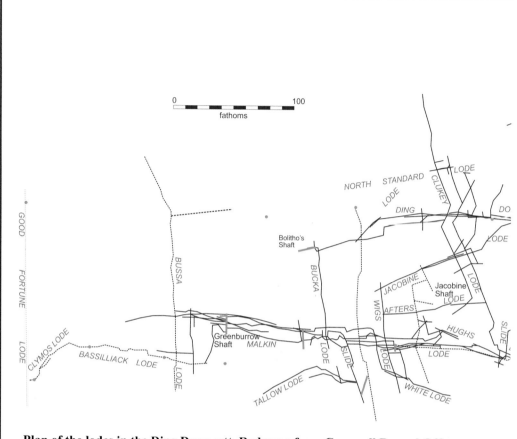

Plan of the lodes in the Ding Dong sett. Redrawn from Cornwall Record Office document MRO 1162-5 (most shafts omitted for clarity)

The North and South or Cross lodes range from 4 to 16 degrees east of south and west of north with an underlie of 45 degrees to the west. They are composed of quartz and capel, often with them a leader of jasper. They are by far the longest lodes of the mine and in many cases seem to be connecting links, and terminations, of bunches of tin. The three largest of these are Good Fortune, Bussa and New Lodes. Where productive these lodes occurred in channels of soft decomposed granite but, in common with other lodes, in depth and unproductiveness, the enclosing granite became very hard, and the lode narrowed. Bucka, Wig, Clukey and several slide lodes had been vastly productive and the united bunches of tin on them had an estimated total length of 1¼ miles and a depth of 20 fathoms.

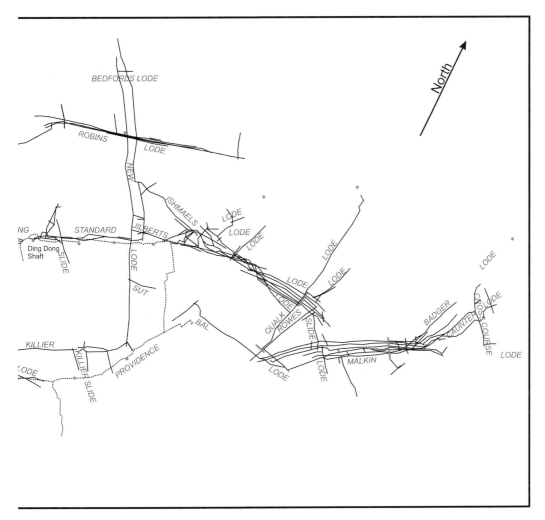

It is a common phenomenon in Cornwall to find that lodes improved in value where they intersected other structures although the sudden impoverishment of a lode at an intersection was not unknown. Hunt wrote: "Sometimes a vertical lode is met with, but it lasts but a few fathoms and usually dies out. Some of the strings lead to a good bunch of tin, but these bunches are not continuous, although they often yield a considerable quantity of ore. No one lode could be traced across the mine and on the whole the lodes were most likely to be echelon structures or parallel veins within zones of mineralised granite. The appearance of the rock is peculiar – it is in granite, with pale green and pale brown feldspar and quartz and dark mica. The granite is coarse-grained, porphyritic (containing large feldspar crystals), and frequently decomposing".[6]

Overall the lodes were small (*i.e.* narrow, more typical of the St Just district) and, according to Hunt, "a lode 12 inches wide was regarded as a wide one". The tin bearing lodes were from one to eighteen inches in width and had an estimated average tin content of 3-4%.[7] Of the mineralisation of this immediate area Hunt stated: "It is not easy to understand how this isolated portion of the granite became so stanniferous, situate as it is in the middle of the great granite mass of West Cornwall, unless we refer the action to heat maintaining a prolonged plastic state after the consolidation of the surrounding portion". The isolated position of the mine was used as an example of an 'emanative centre' by Dines.[8] Essentially an emanative centre was the site where mineralising fluids were presumed to have come out of the granite through pre-existing cracks, rather than creating their own cracks as in the modern theory (as described above). The supposed centres were defined by comparatively restricted zones of high temperature minerals (*i.e.* those of tin and tungsten) surrounded by successively lower temperature mineral zones.

The different mineral zones are still used in Cornish mining geology and Ding Dong Mine is regarded as being at the bottom of the tin zone, beneath which there is no further mineralisation.

The granite was different in both appearance and structure around the productive and non-productive parts of the lodes. Adjacent to productive areas the granite was found to be very lustrous with pearly bright feldspar and greater than normal quantities of muscovite (white mica) diffused throughout the whole rock. Where lodes were unproductive, especially in depth, there was less mica, the feldspar less lustrous, and the rock was much harder with a vitreous appearance; if decomposed (kaolinised) it was duller than usual.

In addition to the complex nature of the lodes, the country rock itself presented some problems in that some sections of the mine were in partially kaolinised granite, known to the miners as 'pot growan'.[9] Kaolinised granite was not an unusual component of the lode although it was usually confined to an area a few centimetres thick on one or both sides of the lode. The method of extracting the ore from such ground was revealed in detail in a conversation between the managing agent, Captain John Truran, and Captain Robert Dunstan, the latter having visited the mine for the purpose of studying the working conditions of the miners as part of a Royal Commission.[10] Captain Truran stated that the men chiselled out the centre of the lode which was softer than the surrounding rock, "They chisel it out with a picker", he added. "They use a hammer and cut away the centre of the lode and bring it out, being soft in the centre, and then they blast the sides". This means of removing the ore was known as 'desuing'.

The possibility of working china clay (*i.e.* decomposed granite) on the mine was discussed in a prospectus of the Ding Dong Mining Syndicate in 1913. Truran further stated that quantities of steatite or soapstone were also found in the lode as well as a substance which they called antimony. The steatite was most likely a variety of china clay, formed from the decomposition of the granite adjacent to the lode or along faults in the granite. There is no evidence to suggest that the 'antimony' was a true antimony ore such as stibnite (Sb_2S_3), and there are no records of any antimony compound in any of the mine's mineral output statistics. Captain Truran merely referred to it as 'what, we call antimony' adding, "but that, I suppose will be found to be mica. It is a sort of oily substance, softer than the surrounding rock and of a different character". There is no recorded reason for the use of the word 'antimony'.

Chapter 4 references

1. Goode, A. J. J., and Taylor, R., 1988. *Geology of the Country around Penzance.* Memoir of the British Geological Survey, Sheets 351 and 358 (England and Wales).

2. 'Capel' is a name given to different features by different authors. In this context it refers to fine-grained tourmaline which may form one or both sides of the lode and which carries tin in variable quantities. This is approximately the same as the lode feature known as 'peach'.

3. Dines, H. G., 1956. *The Metalliferous Mining Region of Southwest England,* pp96-100. HMSO, London.

4. Description of Ding Dong Mine by Thomas Daniel (Trevithick Society document, now at the Cornwall Record Office)

5. Dines, H. G., 1956, *op. cit.*

6. Hunt, R., 1887. *British Mining* (second edition), p351

7. Dines, H. G., 1956, *op. cit.*

8. Dines, H. G., 1956, *op. cit.*

9. Growan: anything in small lumps or grains formed in a mass, its root being Broth (pronounced groh), curds.

10. Lord Kinnaird's *Report on the Conditions in the Metal Mines of Britain,* 1864. HMSO, London.

Chapter 5

Coasters and Coal

Cornwall's Achilles' heel in terms of industry has always been (apart from its isolation) the lack of any coal deposits. Particularly for 19th century industry coal (and coke) was used extensively as a fuel for steam engines and as a heat source for foundries and tin smelters; the lack of coal was the principal reason why copper smelting was established in South Wales. Several railways and tramways were constructed in Cornwall during the middle of the 19th century, notably the Hayle Railway (Hayle-Redruth-Portreath) in 1837 and its westward extension in 1852, but it was not until the opening of Brunel's Royal Albert Bridge at Saltash in 1859 that Cornwall was connected by rail to the rest of England. However, until 1867 there was a break between broad and standard gauge track at Truro, necessitating unloading and reloading between the two incompatible sections. Even after the rationalisation of the railway line the coastal trade remained very important and did not die out until well into the 20th century.[1]

Coal for mine boilers was brought from South Wales (and, occasionally, from Newcastle) by coaster: schooner, lugger, ketch or other, vessels which differed in size and type of rig. The same ships might take copper ore to Wales for smelting. This was common practice among the mines, particularly the coastal mines of the St Just and St Ives districts, and shows the dependence of the mines on the coastal trade routes, particularly with Bristol and South Wales. Depending on a particular mine's location, and possibly the ship's owner, coal would have been landed at Penzance or Hayle, although coal was also available from merchants such as J. B. Coulson & Co. in Penzance, one of Ding Dong's shareholders who also supplied many other local mines.

The brigantine *Henry Harvey* was typical of the coasters which kept Cornwall supplied with goods and also sent Cornish goods elsewhere. She is seen here aground on the Battery Rocks, Penzance, in March 1896. Five persons onboard were rescued by lifeboat. *Cornwall Centre.*

Just before Christmas 1868 a scheme to build a harbour for St Just was reported in the newspapers.[2] This project would have been a huge undertaking as it was to include breakwaters up to 130 feet length and piers up to 700 feet. However, it was not mentioned again in the local press and was presumably turned down by the Board of Trade, for reasons unknown, although it would probably have been the only harbour in the country with a dangerous reef just outside it. Had the scheme worked however, it would have been tremendously useful for the mining interests in the area as it would have made transport, especially of bulk materials, to and from the mines much easier and cheaper.

A number of vessels are mentioned in the mine's cost books. The majority, such as *Francis Griffiths*, *Alert*, *Tell Tale* and *Eleanora*, had unknown owners although some are known to have been operated by Welsh collieries. The *Mary Boyns* however was a local ship, owned by the Boyns family which ran Wheal Owles, near St Just. This schooner was launched in June 1858, named for the wife of the nephew of Richard 'Purser' Boyns, and was lost some years later after being rammed by the Whitby steamer *Mulgrave* off Godrevy.[3] The *Lafrowda* was undoubtedly owned by a family or company with connections with St Just, possibly the Boyns family, the James family (Botallack Mine), the Holman family (St Just Foundry, Penzance Dry Dock and various mines) or some other. It seems likely that the very fast schooner *Killiow* was owned by someone with connections with Ding Dong Mine, possibly even the Bolitho family (although there is a barton of the same name, formerly owned by the smelter J. C. Daubuz of Truro). Another schooner, the *Elizabeth Ann*, may have been owned by the Bolithos, named for Elizabeth Ann Bolitho.

The *Alice Williams* was built by James Bevans in his Llanelli shipyard in 1854. She was launched in December 1854 and registered at Falmouth on 9 January 1855. The ship measured 80.8 feet in length, 20.5 feet in breadth and her hold was 11.8 feet deep; she weighed 137 tons. She had a single deck, two masts, a square stern and a female bust figurehead, said to be of the wife of the principal owner. Much of her trade was carrying coal to Devon and Cornwall

The *Alice Williams*, **unknown location. Note the numerous repairs to the sails, showing the hard life of the ship.** *Cornwall Centre.*

from Wales and returning with ore. In the summer months she made voyages further afield to Scandinavia, Northern Spain and France, mostly carrying coal, iron ore and timber. From 1885 her main trade was mostly based at Par and Pentewan carrying china clay or granite for a variety of ports in England and Scotland and returning to Cornwall with coal.

In February 1928, the *Alice Williams* was bound from north-west England with a cargo of 100 tons of coal.[4,5] After encountering strong winds off the Pembrokeshire coast she was abandoned by her crew who, having lost control of her and believing that she would founder, left her and were picked up by a trawler off St Ann's Head and taken to safety in Milford Haven. The ship did not succumb immediately and drifted into a small cove on the south east coast of Skokholm Island at a place still known as Wreck Cove. She became stuck fast, with her bowsprit and rudder broken and her sails hanging. Her cargo of coal, as well as many other items, was salvaged. She was considered a total wreck and, after negotiations, was bought by Ronald Lockley (the island's tenant), for £5. According to Lockley "she supplied the material for repairing the roofless house and the coal lasted several years in Wreck Cove where it was piled high and used by the sea birds to nest in". The ship's figurehead now looks down over the landing stage in South Haven.

Coasters mentioned in the cost books are: *Agenoria, Agnes, Albeona, Albert, Alert, Alexander, Amity, Ann, Arab, Beryl, British Lady, Celerity, Charlotte, Chyandour, Drake, Edward, Eleanora, Elizabeth Ann, Flash, Foxhole, Francis Griffiths, George Williams, Glasbrook, Harmony, Henry Harvey, Herald, Hurrell, Jane, John, Killiow, Lafrowda, Magie, Marianne, Mary, Mary Boyns, Newcastle, Pembrey, Prima Donna, Swift, Tell Tale, Union, Venus, William*

Chapter 5 references

1. Carter, C., 1998. *The Port of Penzance*. Black Dwarf Publications, Lydney.
2. *Cornish Telegraph* 23.12.1868
3. Clive Carter, personal communication
4. Website: http://members.aol.com/skokholm/alice.htm
5. Bainbridge, G., 1980. *The Wooden Ships and the Iron Men of the Cornish China Clay Trade*. Charlestown Estates Ltd., Charlestown.

Chapter 6

The Origins of Ding Dong Mine

Determining the precise date of commencement of the first period of working proves an impossible task, and such documentary evidence we have is conflicting. According to Thomas Bolitho, the principal shareholder in the mine at the time of the 1878 closure, it had been worked for two hundred years without interruption, giving a starting date of around 1678. Contrary to this, in August 1856, the *Mining Journal* reported that operations had been carried on for a continuous period of more than 120 years, indicating a start around the year 1736. Meanwhile, Richard Tredinnick, a London stockbroker (later bankrupted), noted that the mine had been at work upwards of 100 years without cessation, giving a start date of around 1750.

In 1861 Captain James Nancarrow reported that the mine had been at work from a very distant period, and from the last hundred years without intermission (1761),[1] whilst Thomas Spargo, a share-broker and mining engineer, stated that the mine had been regularly worked under the Bolitho family and their ancestors for the previous hundred years, and long before the commencement of that period,[2] which indicates a start well before 1768. Later sources were less traditional and more authoritative. Kelly's *Directory of Cornwall*, 1873, whose main source of information was the mining company itself, states that the majority of shares had been held by the Bolitho family for 120 years, thus indicating the starting of the mine as being 1753.[3] In 1877 Richard Wellington, the purser of the company, noted that the Bolithos had had an interest in the mine for 130 years, *i.e.* since 1747.[4]

That the mine was worked in the previous century cannot be entirely discounted, but if there was any activity at that time, the working most

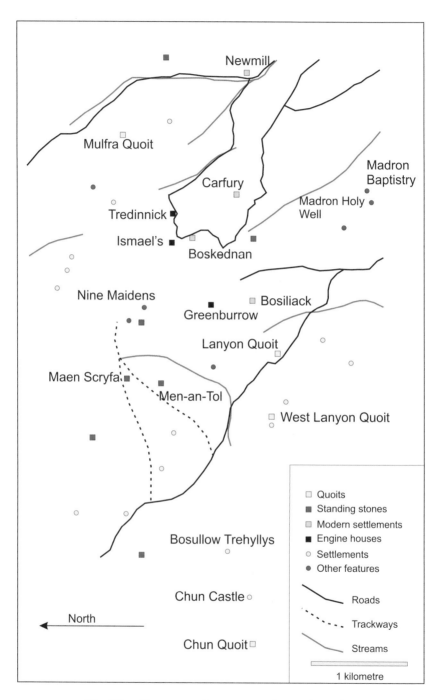

The Ding Dong area showing nearby ancient sites.

certainly did not go by the name Ding Dong. The origins of the tin industry in this area of West Penwith precede the above mentioned dates by some two thousand years. In 1925 excavations at the Iron Age hill fort of Chun Castle, near Pendeen, revealed a series of small tin smelting pits, in one of which was found a 5.4kg lump of tin slag.[5] This, and other, evidence clearly indicates that West Cornwall was already a tin producing region of importance and the numerous remains of early settlements and burial chambers scattered about the surrounding moorland bear further witness to this.

Archaeological remains such as those found at Chun Castle give us an insight into this early period, but on the subject of written accounts of the tin trade between Cornwall and the Mediterranean, we are still very much in the dark. Homer mentions tin as forming a corselet (a piece of armour) presented by the King of Cyprus to Agamemnon, the legendary leader of Greek forces in the Trojan War (c.1200 BC), thus indicating that tin was known at least twelve centuries before Christ. Herodotus (c.484-c.424 BC), often called 'the father of history', wrote in 440BC: "Neither am I better acquainted with the islands called 'Cassiterides'; from where we are said to have our tin". The latter was an alleged group of ten islands 'vaguely situated in a sea beyond Europe' and also the supposed source from which the Phoenicians obtained their tin.[6]

That the latter traded with Cornwall was once a popular supposition without any tangible evidence and has since been refuted by present scholars. The Phoenician theory was highly popular in the last century, giving rise to many embellished accounts from which other writers freely drew, thus perpetuating a myth.

While it is all too easy to discount stories regarding the production of tin from Ding Dong in the first millennia BC and AD it should be noted that there are a number of Neolithic and Bronze Age-Iron Age sites in the immediate area. Chun Castle to the west has already been mentioned, while the settlement of Bossullow Trehyllys lies just east of it. To the north of the hamlet of Boskednan there are settlements at Bodrifty, while three kilometres east is the major settlement of Chysauster and the hill fort of Castle-an-Dinas. Other signs of habitation lie to the north of Greenburrow. These sites were occupied during the Late Bronze Age and again during the Iron Age.

Important Neolithic sites include Chun Quoit to the west, Men-an-Tol to the north and Lanyon and West Lanyon Quoits to the south and south-west and Mulfra Hill Quoit to the east. There is also a Neolithic entrance grave at Bosilliack. Another major feature of the area is the so-called Tinner's Way, an ancient trackway which can be traced from Cape Cornwall to St Ives.

Lines of shallow shafts and lode-back workings on the moor to the north-west of the Greenburrow engine house. *Cornwall Historic Environment Services.*

A more definitive outline emerged some eight years before the birth of Christ in the writings of the Sicilian Greek historian and geographer Diodorus Siculus.[7,8] In his major work *Bibliotheca Historica*,[9] a work of some forty volumes, he gives a reasonably clear description of Britain and furthermore of West Penwith and its inhabitants. He described Britain as being triangular in shape and the promontory nearest mainland Europe was called Cantium (Kent). At the opposite extremity was the promontory known as Belerium (West Penwith) which turned towards the sea 'Orca'. "The inhabitants of Belerium were hospitable", he wrote, "and on account of their intercourse with strangers, civilised in habits". It was they who produced tin which they melted into 'astragali' (knuckle-bone shaped slabs), and carried it to an island in front of Britain called 'Ictis', a peninsula at low tide, where they transported the tin in carts from the shore. Here the traders bought it and carried it into Gaul, across which it was taken on horseback in about thirty days to Marseilles.[10] The geographical location of Ictis, whilst not being fully established, is widely believed to be St Michael's Mount,[11] although 2,500 years ago the Mount would have been a hill on or near the coast and surrounded by forest.

The account by Diodorus was based on an earlier description, written by the Greek traveller-cum-explorer Pytheas. Pytheas was based in what is now Marseilles and in about 275BC made a series of trips, circumnavigating the British Isles. It seems that Pytheas began his journey in Cornwall, presumably because both the land and its inhabitants were known to the people of the western Mediterranean, having a well-established trade in tin by this period.

Of the Roman occupation of Britain (43-410AD) very little is known concerning their influence over the Cornish tin trade. The Romano-British section of the *Victoria History of Cornwall*, a highly inaccurate source, claimed that it was doubtful if the Romans exploited the mines, but other authorities have questioned this, as one wrote:

> "It certainly seems strange that the Romans, being aware of the richness of the tin mines, and accustomed to dealing with other metals in Britain, should have neglected to exploit the Cornish tin workings", and added, "Nevertheless many Roman remains have been found in Cornwall, and it is more than likely therefore that trading posts were established there".[12]

Certainly the Romans operated mines elsewhere in Britain, and Julius Caesar, writing in the first century BC, speaks of tin production in Britain and it is likely that the mineral wealth of the island (as well as its strategic position on the Irish gold trade route) would have been an added incentive for the Roman invasion in 44AD. The lack of any obvious Roman tin production from Cornwall may have two reasons: firstly, the isolation of the mines and attendant logistical problems and, secondly, that the Romans were already producing tin from the Iberian Peninsula, much closer to home.

The Saxon period is equally obscure, apart from a traditional account, dating from around 600AD, concerning an Alexandrian galley which journeyed to Britain, and bore away a load of tin, which legend has it, was miraculously changed into silver on the way.[13]

The documented history of the Cornish tin industry does not begin until the twelfth century, and even then contained little more than lists of figures showing relative output of tin from Devon and Cornwall. Of the actual mines themselves we know nothing but, throughout the 13th, 14th and 15th centuries, the tin trade appears to have been progressive and the tin workings of Cornwall were increasing in size and importance. These early workings either took the form of tin streaming or bounding, the latter method being the searching for tin in either unenclosed land (known as wastrel) or enclosed land (several). Tinners could not enter enclosed land until the owner's permission had been obtained and after this, if mineral was discovered, it lay in the landowner's power either to work it himself, set it out to other miners, or leave it unworked.

In wastrel the tinners could enter freely and search for tin, although again not without certain acknowledgment of the owner's right in the form of 'toll tin' or 'lord's dish'. In early times this was usually of the value of the tin extracted while in later times it was taken prior to the payment of any tax not clear. Originally, bounds were subject to annual renewal, and failure to re-define the area to be worked rendered the tinner to forfeit his claim. It was these early workings that gave rise to some of the most illustrious names in Cornish mining. Such small workings also marked the beginning of Ding Dong.

While many of the apocryphal tales would have the reader believe that mining has been carried out at Ding Dong for over two millennia, the first documentary evidence of mining in the immediate area is a reference to tin bounds registered on 27th June 1507.[14] These were registered by Andrew Jak and partners Harry Thomas Engay and Thomas Treythall and comprised a tin-work in Polerrawe Moor called Whele Veer. John Norden, in his work completed around the end of the 16th century, refers to "A Tynn-worke called

Basilsacke in the parishe of Madderne".[15] This may be an early spelling of 'Bosiliack' which is still marked by a farm of that name situated immediately south of Greenburrow, although a nearby hamlet is called Bosiljack. Of the age and extent of this working we have no knowledge, but to have attracted the attention of Norden it was obviously already a working of some importance and therefore it is justifiable to assume that Bosiliack was the nucleus around which other workings were opened up in the succeeding centuries.

It is likely that all of the streams in the area have been searched for tin over a considerable period of time, with little underground mining not commencing before the 18th century. To the east of the Ding Dong sett is the Try Valley stream, which becomes the Trevaylor Stream after its confluence with another stream which starts just east of Higher Ninnes. The Chyandour Brook commences just north of Mount Whistle and drains the central part of the sett, while another stream runs south from just west of Bosilliack. Finally, the Newlyn River has its origin north-west of the Men-an-Tol and for just under a mile runs parallel to a run of shafts. These streams would have given ample evidence for the existence of tin lodes on the moors.

In 1607 a stamping mill was recorded at Mulfra, no doubt connected to another, unfortunately unrecorded, tin work.[16] There is a further reference to mining close to Bosiliack in the early 17th century under the name of Lanyon Tin Mine, as contained in the following: "There is a Tin work upon the wastrell of Lanyon, and there is a wash thereof made about Michlemas, 1632, of 45 gallons of Tynn, and the 15th part belongeth to the Landlord and the rest to the tinners".[17] In May 1653 there is a reference to the sale of a sixth part of a plot of land "where was sometime one ould paire of Stamps", with sixth part of the plot adjoining, known by the name of Mulfra stamping mill, situated in Villenoy in Madron.[18] It is possible that Villenoy is a slightly altered version of the Cornish Vellanoweth, or New Mill.

The Court Rolls for the Manor of Trezela and Mulfra, owned by Lord Robartes, record tin wrought intermittently during the years 1676 to 1711. These refer to Boskednan Wartha first in 1666, Tredinnick in 1669, Wheal Whiddon in 1670, Croft Dour in 1684, White Works in 1687, Wheal Malkin in 1691, and Wheal an Bussa in 1692. Black tin from Grouse, Tallow and Wheal Malkin was smelted at Angarrack smelting house in 1708-1714, but in very small

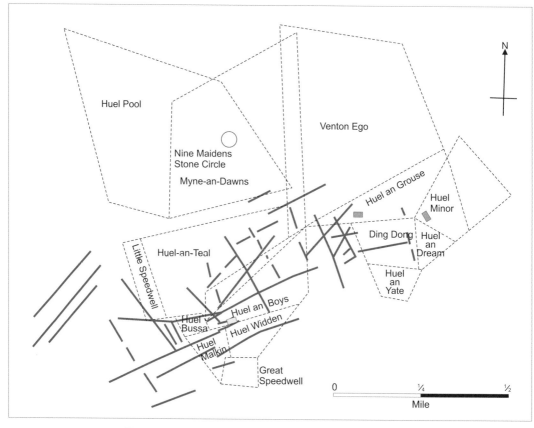

Redrawing of Charles Moody's bounds map of 1782.

quantities compared with other mines in the area. The Godolphin accounts record farm tin received from the Gweall Malkyn tinwork between 1734 and 1745, totalling £17.[19]

Three individual workings are known to have been operating in 1714. These were Good Fortune, Hard Shafts Bounds, and Wheal Malken (or Malkin).[20] Good Fortune Bounds were then the most westerly of the three, situated some 700 yards west-north-west of Greenburrow and 290 yards north-west by west of Bosiliack Shaft, and it would appear that at this time Bosiliack and Good Fortune were one and the same working (SW 431 345). Also to the west lay Wheal Malkin, some 580 yards south-east of Good Fortune (SW 435 343). The exception was Hard Shaft itself (SW 439 349), which lay 700 yards NNE of Greenburrow.[21]

48

These small ventures rapidly increased in number during the first half of the 18th century, as revealed in an indenture, dated 1736, concerning the sale of shares in the following bounds: Wheal an Grouse (SW 444 349), Wheal an Pool (SW 432 352), Venton Ego (SW 441 353), Great Speedwell (SW 436 342) and Little Wheal Whidden (SW 436 343).[22] Most of these were situated in the immediate vicinity of Wheal Malkin, with the exception of Wheal an Pool and the adjoining Nine Maidens or Myne Dawns (SW 435 351), the latter encompassing the stone circle of that name. These two workings lay half-a-mile to the north of Wheal Malkin and the northern boundary of Wheal an Pool almost reached the stone where the four parishes of Morvah, Madron, Zennor and Gulval converge. The bounds of Venton Ego and Wheal an Grouse lay half a mile north-east of Wheal Malkin and about 350 yards north-west of Boskednan Farm.

Although the name 'Ding Dong' appeared on Moody's bounds map in the early 1780s there is, in fact, an earlier reference. According to John Rowe in his book *Cornwall in the Age of the Industrial Revolution* (p17), in 1751 the Reverend Walter Borlase held shares in the sett of Great Wheal Malkin, Little Wheal Malkin, Nine Maids or 'Myne Andrenze', Ventonegue Well and Ding Dong, in Gulval and Madron parishes.

In February 1752 liberty was granted to drive one or more adits from the bottom or west side of Boskednan Wartha tenement.[23] This was intended to be driven into a field called Tallah Bean and "to a certain lode of tin within the tenement of Tredennack commonly called Wheal Malkin Great Lode, and to work the lode; and to drive another drift or adit to Wheal Malkin great lode". In a will dated April 20th 1758 it was stated that one John Harvey of Penzance had entered into an agreement with a Joseph Geach and his wife for the absolute purchase of Wheal Malkin and other tin bounds in the area.[24,25]

Some years later four more names emerged. A document dated March 31st 1764, drawn between Thomas Kniveton of Lelant and Abel Angove of Illogan, referred to an earlier deed dated January 1st 1742 in which one Peter Carveth, late of Nansalverne, assigned a number of West Cornwall bounds which included the following in the parishes of Madron and Gulval: "Adsa Wensack, in the commons of Boskednan and Bosejack (Bosiliack), Whealan-Minnor (SW 445 349), in the common of Bosporth Enys (Bosporthennis), and Wheal-an-Trick in Lanyon Downs". Adsa Wensack was described as "lying between the White Work (Wheal Widden (SW 436 343), possibly a reference to china clay) and The Tallow Hedge Bounds" – two sites on either side of Wheal Malkin.[26]

To this day many still maintain that Ding Dong and Wheal Malkin were one and the same working and that Wheal Malkin was the original name of Ding Dong. This is not borne out by the documentary evidence currently available and the two mines appear to have operated side-by-side under their respective names for a number of years. In 1768, among the effects and estate of William John, a bankrupt and formerly a merchant of Penzance, a number of part shares in various tin mines were sold, and these included 1-30th part in "the original adventure in Wheal Malkin and the Killio Mines in the parishes of Madron and Gulval with the assignees rights in the several tribute pitches there".[27] The latter exploited the eastern end of the Wheal Malkin Lode which, according to an early plan of the sett, was also known as Killio Lode.[28]

In the will of Thomas Hosking of Madron, dated 11th April 1869, a 1-30th share was left to his son Thomas, and a 1-30th share to his other son John, "with all tools, tackle and implements thereto belonging, and release from any monies owing".[29]

The first known publicly advertised sale of shares in Wheal Malkin was in June 1775 when a 30th share was advertised for sale in the *Sherborne & Yeovil Mercury*.[30] Charles Moody's survey of tin bounds, dated 1782, shows sixteen workings extending from Greenburrow to Tredinnick – a distance of almost a mile.[31] Centred immediately about the hamlet of Boskednan were the bounds of Wheal-an-Drean, Wheal Minnor, Wheal-an-Grouse, and a small working covering about ten acres, called 'Ding Dong' (SW 442 347).

Two principal features are illustrated on Moody's plan. The first is the extent of the individual workings from which the future Ding Dong sett evolved, and, secondly, the insignificance of the original Ding Dong working at that time. Also revealed is a distinct east-west division of the complex, with one group of workings centred on Wheal Malkin to the west, and the eastern group around Boskednan and Tredinnick. It was basically from this division that the two principal mines, Wheal Malkin and Ding Dong, emerged and, most important, it was on Moody's bounds map, towards the end of the 18th century, that the name 'Ding Dong' first appeared, which in turn indicates a very strong likelihood that Ding Dong was formerly worked under a different name.

Another possible source of confusion lies in the location of Ding Dong and Wheal Killio (in later years Wheal Killiow). The two mines are very close to each other (Killio at SW 439 348 and Ding Dong at SW 442 347) and in the main 19th century working of Ding Dong the mine had shafts called East, West and South Killiow. East and West Killiow Shafts actually lie within the original Ding Dong and Wheal-an-Yate bounds, the latter centred on SW 442 346.

In June 1786 a one-fifteenth share "of and in all that valuable and very profitable tin mine called Wheal Malkin" was advertised for sale, including "all the tin stuff now lying at grass belonging to the said share".[32] The mine was described as being in an exceedingly good course of working on several promising lodes and a "new patent wind engine now erecting thereon will considerably diminish the water charges". By the end of the following year the wind engine had been erected but circumstances had caused the mine's management to issue the following statement in the *Sherborne & Yeovil Mercury*:

Wheal Malkin Tin Mine

Whereas many malicious and erroneous reports have been industriously propagated to the prejudice of the constructor of the patent wind engine erected on this mine, by which many have been led to believe that the said engine does not answer the purpose for which it was intended; justice therefore to the patentee we think is our duty to declare the said reports are extremely false and the engine drawing the water out of the mine, either by wind or by horses, with the greatest ease; and that it does completely answer our expectations and wishes of the adventurers in every respect.

Wm Thomas purser, manager and book keeper

Thomas Warren, captain[33]

The designer of the wind engine was one Benjamin Heame (also sometimes

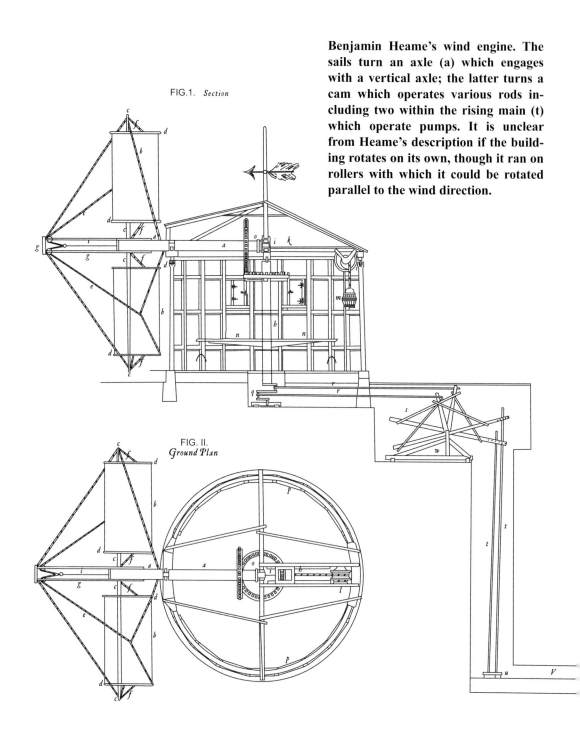

Benjamin Heame's wind engine. The sails turn an axle (a) which engages with a vertical axle; the latter turns a cam which operates various rods including two within the rising main (t) which operate pumps. It is unclear from Heame's description if the building rotates on its own, though it ran on rollers with which it could be rotated parallel to the wind direction.

FIG.1. *Section*

FIG. II.
Ground Plan

spelled Neame), a merchant of Penryn who in 1787 took out a patent for a 'New Invented Method of Regulating the Sails or Vanes of Engines and Mills worked by Force of Wind'.[34] Heame was also a shareholder in both Wheal Malkin and Ding Dong. Heame died just under two years after the newspaper article and part of his estate (together with that of Thomas Treeve, also of Penryn), advertised to be sold by auction in November 1789, included 6-15ths and 1-18th shares in Wheal Malkin, Killiow, and Bosiliack Mines and 1-16th share of Ding Dong Mine.[35] Also advertised was a "one third part of Gear Stamping Mills, with the dwelling house, stables, and premises thereunto belonging, situate in the parish of Gulval, for the remainder of the term of 99 years, determinable on the death of one good life." The location of the windmill is not known; the Wheal Malkin sett in its strictest sense lies to the southwest of Greenburrow Shaft but in the wider sense is centred on that shaft. This inclined shaft would not have been suitable for pumping by this means but could have been used for winding.

The exact location of the Gear Stamping Mills is also not known but may lie to the north-east of Higher Gear (on the Penzance road about 750m SSE of New Mill and about 2km south-east of Tredinnick) on the south bank of the Chyandour stream; possibly it dealt with some of the produce of the various mines. East Ding Dong Mine was renting Gear stamps in 1856 (see Chapter 11).

In June 1792, Andrew Stevens of Gulval, on behalf of himself and Ding Dong adventurers, was given liberty to drive an adit from the east end of the Killio adit into Ding Dong Mine. All tin raised within the limits of Killiow sett was reserved for the use of the lords and adventurers of Killiow Mine. The Duke of Leeds was given permission to "drive any adit or use any shaft" within the sett.[36]

In August 1792, Boskednan and Carfury in Madron were set to be worked by at least four "able workmen", for a minimum period of six months per year "unless hindered by water or some unforeseen Accident". Any part of the sett remaining unworked for more than six months was to be set to other adventurers; the takers were to have liberty to take off Ding Dong eastern adit and drive it into Wheal Providence sett and to drive the adit if necessary through Boskednan and Carfury. All tin raised in the limits of the Ding Dong

Sale of Heame's and Treeve's shares in various mines; *Sherborne Mercury*

sett were to be reserved to the lords of Ding Dong.[37]

In December 1793 a 1-16th share of Ding Dong, property of the late Mrs Phillipa Usticke, was advertised for sale (in January 1794).[38] In the correspondence between William Carne and Messrs Boulton and Watt (largely regarding Bull and Trevithick's alleged infringement of their patents, see Chapter 6) it appears that the mine was then in a poor state. On 27 June 1795 Thomas Wilson, Boulton and Watt's legal representative in Cornwall, wrote to Carne stating that "there was some reason to expect an application from Ding Dong Advrs, to settle the Disputes now at Issue, betwixt them & Boulton & Watt". The latter were in no mood to accept any sort of compromise regarding the dues owed them: "Stop the Mine, or run the risk of incurring the Chancellor's displeasure by continuing to work on".[39] In reply, on 10 July 1795, Carne stated that the engine had been stopped (possibly because of the legal situation) and that the mine had not paid cost for the last six months.[40] The mine was in "dept" to Carne for £2,145 and the Lords had reduced their dues from 1-18th to 1-36th for at least two years. Another engine would be required and the mine would not work for the winter. On 8th October 1795 A. Weston wrote to Thomas Wilson stating that the mine would be "utterly ruined" if operations were delayed for another month.[41]

Several times in the 18th century local over-population combined with poor corn harvests provoked food riots. It was these riots that made James Watt, never fond of the local population in any case, to recommend that soldiers be stationed in Truro and Redruth. In March 1795 William Jenkin mentions that, because of the high price of corn demanded by unsympathetic farmers, miners from Wheal Malkin and Ding Dong as well as un-named St Just mines rushed into Penzance to try to liberate food.[42] The residents of the town, aided by men from local villages, staved off the attack. These were desperate times indeed for the poor of the county.

In September 1797 a 1-32nd share was advertised for sale, the mine being described as "now in a most promising state of adventure".[43] The mine had a fire (steam) engine and a very profitable lode, the Killio, had recently been discovered. The manager at this time was Thomas Gundry junior of Goldsithney, a member of the well-known mining family. A 1-32nd share was advertised for sale in August 1778 but it is not known if this was the same share.[44]

The closing years of the eighteenth century witnessed the beginning of mining on a larger scale and, as the mines increased in depth, more capital

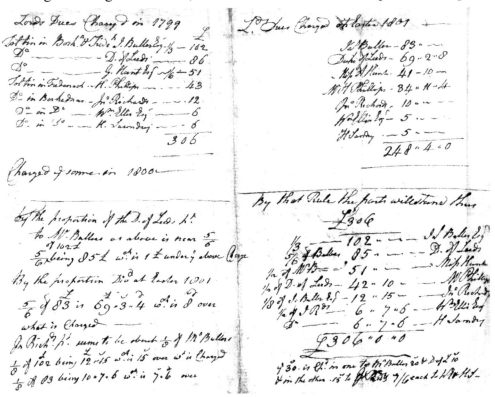

List of Lords' dues for 1799 to 1801.
Cornwall Record Office document DDX 173/89

was required to work them successfully. An increasing number of small-scale workings had either amalgamated to form larger ventures, or were jointly worked whilst retaining their original names. Wheal Malkin was now, by the mid 1790s, the predominant working in the area and was rapidly becoming a separate entity to Ding Dong and her satellites, having absorbed the greater number of bounds to the west.

This period had been a complicated one for Cornish tin mining. For some time prior to the 1790s the industry had been in a very depressed state, exacerbating the generally poor socio-economic conditions of the mining areas. In 1789 the Honourable East India Company commenced the carriage of tin to China, although this firstly required an Act of Parliament to remove the duty applied to "unwrought Tin exported to any Countries beyond the Cape of Good Hope".[45] There were two principal benefits for the tin producers (*i.e.* the tin smelters), the first being the removal of surplus tin from the home market and the second being the higher price which could be forced with lower supplies at home. A small loss would be made on selling the tin abroad but it was considered that this would be outweighed by the benefits. Unfortunately this period brought the Cornish tin industry into some disrepute as, in their hurry to export the metal after a dramatic rise in its price, little regard was paid to the quality, so much so that "the Tin smelters sent these stockings to the East India Compy. in London and have consistently sent them a very impure quality, Iron, old stamp heads, base metal, etc., etc".

Wheal Providence, a working later incorporated into the sett, lay to the east of Ding Dong but the exact location cannot now be determined. However, some indication of its whereabouts are revealed in a letter dated February 6th, 1798,

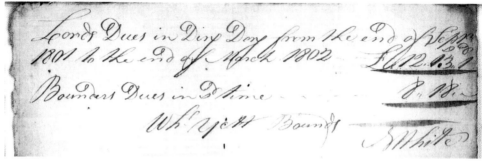

Amount of Lords' dues from September 1801 to March 1802.
Cornwall Record Office document DDX 173/90

written by William Jenkin of Trewirgie, Redruth, to one of the landowners, George Hunt Esq., and ran as follows:

> Respecting John Edmunds' request that thee would be pleased to take off his hands 1-32nd share in Wheal Providence in the Manor of Trezela and Mulfra – the mine adjoins those two capital ones called Ding Dong and Killio, and both lodes run into Wheal Providence sett. It is therefore, judged to be a kindly venture, but the rock is hard and the great bodies of tin in the other mines have been found to be very deep – poor John, and I fear some other adventurers, are getting out of their depth. John went into the concern with a determination of getting himself to be a rich man – but alas he, like many others, forgot to sit down first and count the cost. His growing family will not allow him to continue it any longer, and such are his present circumstances that a less sum than the cost he is out will not relieve him from distress. This being the state of the case, John is desirous of casting himself on thy generosity.[46]

Wheal Providence may thus represent an early working of Mulfra Hill Mine, later East Ding Dong Mine.

In 1799 the bounders of Boskednan and Tredinnick, receiving their dues from tin sales, were listed as J. Buller, the Duke of Leeds, G. Hunt, H. Phillips, Jno. Richards, Wm. Ellis and H. Jason, in decreasing order of the amount of their dues.[47] The total amount of bounders' dues paid in this year was £306.

Although the process of amalgamation had begun in the late 18th century, the general layout was still somewhat fragmentary, particularly around the eastern portion of the complex. At the beginning of the 19th century some nine separate workings were in operation and these appear to have been worked in a more or less sporadic manner. Around the year 1800 it was said that the adventurers in Tincroft Mine, Illogan, had recently made an application for a new sett in consequence of the termination of their existing lease. This was followed by a lengthy dispute with the Lords in granting a renewal. However, readiness to comply was shown by a Miss Hunt who, it was reported, signified her willingness to grant a new sett on a 21-year lease, commencing November 5th, 1802. William Jenkin, in a letter to the Tincroft adventurers, declared that Miss Hunt was in receipt of dues from various mines of which she was either

An acct. of Tin Stuff risen in Dg. Dong Whl Unity
Killio & Jacabine for March & April months 1807

Takers Names	[w]hole No. of BT	value	£	s	d
Matt: Patt Severals	84-	@ 21-	88	4	-
John Bennetts	140-	@ 11/6	80	10	-
Wm Daniell	28-	@ 10/6	14	14	-
Tho$_s$ White	59-	@ 25/6	75	4	6
Tho$_s$ Grenfell	112-	@ 11/6	64	8	-
Wm Waren	4¾	@ 9-	2	2	9
Tho$_s$ Guy	76-	@ 17/3	65	11	-
Wm Daniel	16-	@ 2/3	1	16	-
Mark Daniel	102-	@ 1/9	8	18	6
Do	9½	@ 12/9	6	1	1½
Stephn Nicholls	81-	@ 10/6	42	10	6
Henry Cock Killio	60-	@ 9-	27	-	-
Phillip Maddren	30-	@ 28/6	42	15	-
Bf	802¼	Sev £	519	15	4½
Wm Noy in bounds	39-	@ 18-	25	7	-
Robert Tinner	17-	@ 2/6	2	2	6
Henry Nicholls	36	@ 4/3	7	13	-
Vivian Stevens	72	@ 6-	21	12	-
Wm Thomas	47	@ 16-	37	12	-
Do	26	@ 5/6-	7	3	-
Wm Lawry	92	@ 11/9	54	1	-
James Mann	18-	@ 14-	12	12	-
Nath$_n$ Eddy	10	@ 5/6	2	15	-
Do	6⅓	@ 23/6	7	8	10
Do	18	@ 2/9	2	9	6
Rich$_d$ Beny Jacabine Do	84-	@ 18/5	77	7	-
Henry Phillips	37½	@ 23/6	44	1	3
Phillip Eddy	20	@ 25/2	25	3	4
Edward Eddy	36	@ 16/6	29	14	-
Henry Trembath	15	@ 28/9	21	11	3
Henry Phillips	3½	@ 13/4	2	6	8
Do	1-	@ 10/8	--	10	8
Phillip Eddy	14	@1/7	1	2	2
bounds Bf	592⅓		£ 382	12	2

Received Mr Bullen part £23.9.3

Tin sales from Ding Dong, Wheal Unity, Killiow Mine and Jacobine Mine for March and April 1807. Cornwall Record Office document F/3/113.

part or sole proprietor, and among these were Ding Dong, Wheal Malkin and Wheal Providence.[48]

There was still trade in shares in the mines during 1800, with a 1-32nd share of Ding Dong being advertised in March and 1-16th in Ding Dong, 1-30th in Wheal Malkin and Killiow Mine and 2-10ths in Wheal Providence advertised in July.[49,50] In 1801 Thomas Gundry was still one of the co-adventurers of the Ding Dong operation.[51] According to the journal of the Helston attorney, Christopher Wallis, who held shares in many mining ventures, the purser of Ding Dong, from 1795 to 1807 was Andrew Stephens, and Thomas Edwards held office as clerk from 1803 to 1807. Stephens, or Stevens, had been working the mine in 1792. In 1805 the mine was in 30 shares.[52]

In June 1806 a survey was held at Wheal Malkin for the sale of a 24½-inch cylinder steam engine which had recently been turned into a double-acting engine;[53] the odd size suggests that the cylinder had been re-bored. The sale also included 22 fathoms of 6-inch pumps and 20 fathoms of 4-inch pumps, "not in the least injured or corroded". About the same time (1807) Wheal Killiow, along with two other small mines, Wheal Unity and Wheal Jacobine (pronounced 'Jacka Bean'), were said to be working as one on tribute under the management of Captain Stephens,[54] the latter in all probability the former purser of Ding Dong. This coincided with another merger revealed in a circular printed around 1810, which dealt with the rules and regulations of a miner's club established in Ding Dong, Wheal Boys, Good Fortune, Bossiliack (then referred to as Bossiliack Consolidated Mines) and Wheal Malkin.[55] The latter was now under separate management to Ding Dong and was entering its final years as an independent concern.

During this year Ding Dong Engine Shaft was sunk to 62 fathoms, but workings elsewhere were down to 98 fathoms below adit, the tin and water being raised to the 62 by manual labour. A report for the mineral Lords condemned this practice, and it was proposed that a new adit should be driven from near Ninnis.[56] Ding Dong Engine Shaft is located at SW 43918 34814 and equates with Willey's Shaft, shown on the modern 1:2500 Ordnance Survey map as Witheys Shaft.

Wheal Malkin was offered for sale in 1813[57] and was reported to have been purchased by Captain John Hosking, late of the Mount's Bay Yeomanry. The sale advertisement also mentioned New Wheal Malkin in Zennor, apparently a copper mine. In 1817, 12-57th "parts, shares or doles of and in all that tin mine or adventure for tin called Old Wheal Malkin together with like parts, shares or doles of tin and tin stuff and other produce, engines and other machineries, tools, tackles and materials, which belong to the said mine or adventure Old Wheal Malkin Tin Mine" was sold pursuant to a decree made by the Vice-Warden of the Stannaries (the Right Worshipful John Thomas, Esq.).[58] The case had been between Thomas and another against Hosking the younger (presumably Captain John) and had been heard on January 1st. The cause of the dispute is not known but the name of the Captain was given as James Eddy.

It has previously been mentioned that Ding Dong and Wheal Malkin are often erroneously intertwined. It is true that after 1814, after all of the smaller setts had amalgamated into what was to become Ding Dong Mine, Wheal Malkin was then absorbed into the complex but the first edition of the one inch to one mile Ordnance Survey map, published in 1813, clearly shows the two as separate mines. The exact date of the final amalgamation is not known, however, and it may even have taken place following a period of abandonment of Wheal Malkin.

By 1818 Captain John Hosking was the sole owner of the mine who then, it was said, worked the mine more to the profit of the miners than himself,[59] but two years later, on May 23rd, with the mine's affairs in total disarray, the company was wound up in the Vice-Warden's Court, and the machinery, including horse whim, count house furniture and 18-inch and 21-inch cylinder engines, were advertised for sale.[60]

Captain Hosking, known locally as 'Pusser' (purser) Hosking, employed a mule driver who went by the nick-name of 'Ralfrey'. According to local tradition the miners, passing to and from their work, used to take pleasure in teasing the bad-tempered animals, but the mules often showed their resentment by marking the miners with hoof and teeth and gave chase to anyone who ventured on the moor, except the boys who brought them their oaten straw in winter, and Ralfrey who was as fond of the mules as if they had been brothers. When filing along the lanes laden with sacks of ore, anyone

View of the remains of the stamps engine house and possible boiler house from the west, with Ishmael's whim in the background. *Tony Clarke.*

View of Ding Dong from the east over what appears to be a rather barren landscape, prior to the large-scale removal of the dumps. The various buildings on the dressing floors can be seen left of centre, just below the horizon. *Tony Clarke.*

Old postcard view of the Tredinnick engine house. *Doug Luxford.*

View of Ishmael's whim engine house, showing the north wall of the boiler house.
Doug Luxford.

calling out teasingly to them caused them to leave the train and show fright in spite of Ralfrey's efforts to restrain them. From these traits there originated the common saying applied to a teasy person, "Like Pusser Hosking's moyles – wa-ant bear jesting".[61]

Chapter 6 references

1. *Mining Journal* 5.10.1861
2. Spargo, T., 1868. *The Mines of Cornwall and Devon*. Emily Faithfull, London, p197
3. Cornwall Record Office document DDX 745, the Brooke Index
4. Ibid
5. Jenkin, A. K. Hamilton, 1972. *The Cornish Miner*. David & Charles, p28
6. Earl, B., 1968. *Cornish Mining,* Bradford Baron Ltd., Truro, and Smith G., 1963. *The Cassiterides*, Longman, Green, Longman and Roberts, London.
7. Hunt, R., 1887. *Historical Sketch of British Mining*. EP publishing, UK reprint, p2
8. Diodorus undoubtedly based his account on that of Pytheas (c.380-c.310 BC) who circumnavigated the British Isles between 330 and 320BC. Pytheas's writing has also been used by Pliny the Elder and Strabo (among others); unfortunately his own work, *On The Ocean*, has not survived him.
9. *Encyclopaedia Britannica* vol.4
10. Hunt, R., 1887. *Historical Sketch of British Mining*. EP publishing, UK reprint, p19
11. Hatcher, J., 1973. *English Tin Production and Trade before 1550*. Clarendon Press, p12, and Halliday, F. E., 1959. *A History of Cornwall*, Duckworth, London, p44.
12. Peter, O. The Romans in Cornwall. *Journal of the Royal Institute of Cornwall* XV, II
13. Hatcher, J., 1973 *op. cit,* p12
14. Buckley, J. A., 1987. Tudor Tin Bounds. Penhellick Publications, Cornwall..
15. Norden, J., 1728. Speculi Brianniæ pars: a topographical and historical account .... William Pearson, London.
16. Buckley, J. A., 1987 *op. cit.*
17. Henderson MS volume 19, Royal Institution of Cornwall.
18. Cornwall Record Office document CL/1293
19. Information per Alasdair Neill

20. A. K. Hamilton Jenkin - *Tin Bounds under Parishes* (MS note. - Redruth Cornish Studies Library)

21. Writer's annotated map and Dines, H. G., 1956. *The Metalliferous Mining Region of Southwest England.* HMSO London, p97

22. Cornwall Record Office document DDX 61/8

23. Cornwall Record Office document RH/1/3163

24. Document regarding the sale of tin bounds per the late Clive Carter.

25. Cornwall Record Office document WH/6193

26. Cyril Noall Papers, Royal Institution of Cornwall.

27. Documents dated 1768 per the late Clive Carter.

28. Copied in the library of the Royal Geological Society of Cornwall.

29. Cornwall Record Office document reference volume 9, p 476 - LDS Film No. 0090197 (from members.iimctro.com.au/~rosewarne/probate1.PDF)

30. *Sherborne & Yeovil Mercury* 19.6.1775

31. Courtney Library document B/16/1: Tin Bounds of the parishes of Madron, Gulval, Zennor, St Just, Ludgvan, Towednack, Sancreed, Paul, Morvah and Sennen, 1782; Charles Moody Collection, Royal Institution of Cornwall, Truro

32. *Sherborne & Yeovil Mercury* 19.6.1786

33. *Sherborne & Yeovil Mercury* 24.12.1787

34. Patent 1588 of 1 February 1787

35. *Sherborne & Yeovil Mercury* 23.11.1789

36. Cornwall Record Office document RH/1/3166

37. Cornwall Record Office document RH/1/3162

38. *Sherborne & Yeovil Mercury* 30.12.1793

39. Cornwall Record Office document AD1583/8/34, Boulton and Watt papers

40. Cornwall Record Office document AD1583/8/57, Boulton and Watt papers

41. Cornwall Record Office document AD1583/8/79, Boulton and Watt papers

42. Jenkin, A. K. H., 1951. *News from Cornwall.* Westaway Books, London. p32.

43. *Sherborne & Yeovil Mercury* 11.9.1797

44. *Sherborne & Yeovil Mercury* 27.8.1798

45. Barton, D. B., 1967. *A History of Tin Mining and Smelting in Cornwall.* Bradford Barton Ltd., Truro.

46. Jenkin, A. K. Hamilton, 1972., *op. cit.* p53

47. Cornwall Record Office document DDX 173/89

48. *Observations to the Adventurers in Tincroft Mine by a Cornishman,* 1802. Tin

Pamphlets in the Morrab Library, Penzance, *and* Jenkin, A. K., Hamilton, 1951, *op. cit.*, p36

49. *Sherborne & Yeovil Mercury* 3.3.1800

50. *Sherborne & Yeovil Mercury* 14.7.1800

51. Cornwall Record Office document RH/1/3167

52. William Jenkin letters, Brooke Index DDX 745, Cornwall Record Office

53. *Royal Cornwall Gazette* 31.5.1806

54. Letter from Thomas to William Davy dated July 1807 per Justin Brooke

55. Cornwall Record Office document Brooke Index DDX 745, Cornwall Record Office

56. Information per Alasdair Neill

57. *Royal Cornwall Gazette* 1.5.1813

58. *Royal Cornwall Gazette* 18.1.1817

59. *The Cornishman* 7.2.1957, article by Charles Hoare (Penzance Old Cornwall Society)

60. *The Royal Cornwall Gazette* 1.7.1820

61. *The Cornishman* 7.2.1957

Chapter 7

Ned Bull, Richard Trevithick and the
Topsy-Turvy Engine

As the workings became deeper, early methods of draining the mines were either by numerous adits driven from the principal areas of working or by means of rag and chain pumps, but whether steam power was used in this area before the close of the 18th century is very doubtful. It has been suggested, without any substantial evidence, that Ding Dong Mine was originally equipped with a Newcomen engine,[1] and William Borlase in *The Natural History of Cornwall*, 1758, names a dozen specific mines "and some others" as possessing fire engines (the old term for a steam pumping engine), but although Borlase mentioned twelve mines, the actual number employing steam power at this period could well have been double that number. Barton states: "William Borlase, although a careful observer, was covering too wide a field to be exhaustive in detail"[2] (but see reference 1). Certainly there is no mention of such machinery in the vicinity of Wheal Malkin and Bosiliack at this time, and if there had been steam power in use it seems very unlikely that it would have gone unnoticed by Borlase whose family had a large interest in many of the West Penwith mines. Additionally, there appears to be no mention of steam or fire engines in newspaper advertisements prior to 1797; the presence of such equipment would not have been omitted as it would have added to the importance of a mine's standing.

Barton's reference to a Newcomen engine at Ding Dong prior to 1774 certainly raises a question, however. K. M. Rogers, in *The Newcomen Engine in the West of England* makes no reference to Ding Dong, or indeed to any mine in that area, thus rendering the supposition all the more questionable. The only definitive reference to any sort of engine prior to 1790 is to Heame's patent wind engine. The picture regarding engines on the mine only becomes clearer in the last decade of the 18th century, due to the legal dispute between Richard Trevithick, junior and the celebrated engine manufacturers, Messrs. Boulton and Watt.

James Watt came to Cornwall in 1777 to supervise the erection of one of his engines at Ting Tang Mine in the parish of Gwennap. He was not enthusiastically received by the Cornish mining engineers nor, it was said, was he impressed by the "barbarous country and its inhabitants" but his engine was extremely successful and was a vast improvement on the Newcomen engine.

The latter worked on the principle of a piston working in a vertical open-topped cylinder which was mounted directly above a boiler. Steam at a pressure only fractionally above that of the atmosphere could be admitted at will to the closed end of the cylinder below the piston. The steam was then condensed by means of a jet of water, allowing atmospheric pressure to force down the piston and consequently impart movement to the pump rod in the shaft via the rocking motion of the overhead beam. The repetition of this process in alternately admitting steam and water into the cylinder generated power sufficient to pump water from greater depths than with a Newcomen engine.

This in itself was a huge step forward, but the Newcomen engine also had the disadvantage that relatively enormous quantities of fuel were required. Cornwall depended on Wales for coal and apart from the cost of carriage by sea and over land there was also the matter of import duty which was levied on all coal brought into Cornwall by sea. Various methods were tried to improve the performance of the engines, but to little avail. The only means of meeting demand for greater pumping power was to increase the cylinder diameter on later engines.

Watt's improved engine employed a separate condenser, resulting in greater economy of steam usage, the cylinder being continuously hot and the condenser continuously cool instead of having one vessel needing to be alternately heated and cooled. The new engine was a complete transformation from Newcomen's atmospheric type and was the first true steam engine, in that steam rather than the atmosphere was the actual driving force (although the pressure of the steam was barely greater that of the atmosphere).[3]

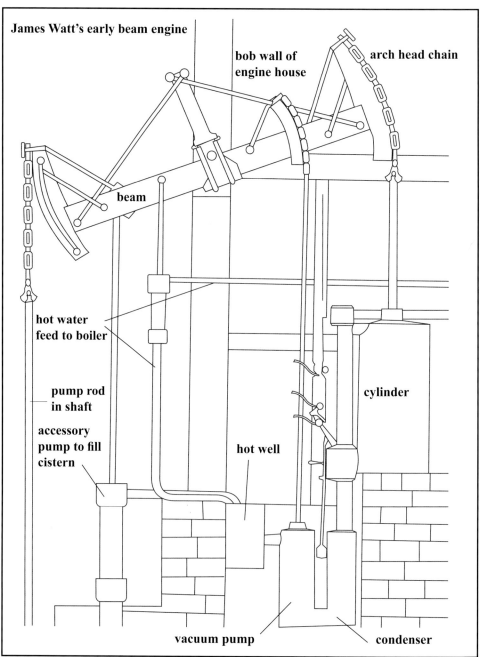

James Watt's early beam engine

bob wall of engine house

arch head chain

beam

hot water feed to boiler

pump rod in shaft

accessory pump to fill cistern

cylinder

hot well

vacuum pump

condenser

By the end of 1778 five of the new engines were at work in Cornwall, using only a quarter of the fuel consumed by the Newcomen type, but Watt, and his partner Matthew Boulton, demanded their reward and stipulated that all mine

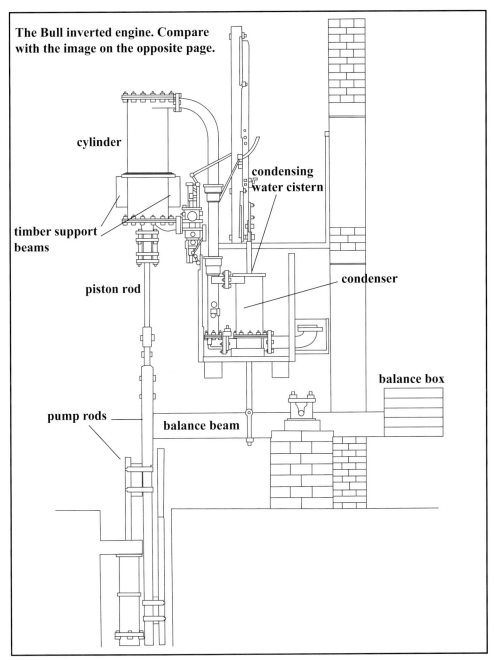

The Bull inverted engine. Compare with the image on the opposite page.

cylinder

condensing water cistern

timber support beams

piston rod

condenser

balance box

pump rods

balance beam

owners using their engines had to sign contracts promising payment of premiums equal to one-third of the value of coal saved. This resulted in numerous attempts to circumvent Watt's patent, to benefit from his invention and to avoid paying the premiums,[4] and the situation was further aggravated in 1792 when, according to tradition, Edward Bull erected an inverted type engine at Balcoath Mine, in the parish of Wendron. However it is no longer believed that Bull's engine was erected at Balcoath, although where this engine was installed is not known.

Bull had been one of Boulton and Watt's chief engine erectors (although he appears to have started his career as an engine man at Bedworth Colliery)[5] and was credited with having invented an engine in which the cylinder was placed directly over the shaft with the piston and rod connected below directly to the pit-work. But Bull, it appears, never did lay claim to having invented it. Actually it was not a new arrangement, for Watt had devised it in 1765 but had put it aside in favour of the beam engine, and in 1776 or 1777 the Cumberland-born iron-master John Wilkinson (1728-1808) had built an engine on the principle of Watt's early engines to power a cylinderboring machine. As this engine was of the 'inverted' type it was consequently referred to as the 'Topsy-Turvy Engine'.[6]

Despite Bull's denial regarding the invention, Boulton and Watt brought an injunction against him on the completion of his engine on the grounds that he had infringed their patent, but the question as to whether Bull had in fact pirated Watt's design remains unanswered. Many described him as an engineer of 'no great ability or originality' who was being manipulated by the Cornish mine captains in a renewed attack on the Boulton and Watt monopoly, and on the 22nd of March, 1794 the Lord Chancellor granted an injunction, restraining him from erecting any more engines on the Watt principle, and from completing those already in hand.[7]

As well as installing one at the Halamanning Mines, near St. Hilary, both Bull and Richard Trevithick were also engaged upon erecting an engine at Ding Dong. It should be noted that Richard Trevithick, well-known during his later life, was here working as Bull's lesser-known assistant. Edward Bull was at this time far better known than his young colleague and his untimely death in 1797 cut short a promising life.[8]

Bull had asked the court for permission to complete the Ding Dong and Halamanning engines, but his request was denied. Following this, Thomas

The protagonists: top left: James Watt; top right: James Watt junior; bottom left: William Murdoch; bottom right: Matthew Boulton.

Left: Richard Trevithick

No images are known of Edward Bull or Thomas Wilson.

71

Weston, the solicitor acting for Boulton and Watt, stated in a letter dated June 11th 1795 that ". . . .the Lord Chancellor has this day granted an Injunction against using the Engine at Ding Dong Mine. Mr Trevethic Junr could not be included as he had not been made a party to the Suit, but if you will send me his Christian name, I will take care to prevent his future intermeddling: and further if you can send me an affidavit that Trevethic is Bull's Partner or his known agent, I will apply to the Court to grant an Attachment against Bull for his contempt".[9]

Further attempts to ascertain as to whether Trevithick was working in partnership with Bull proved fruitless. In a letter to Boulton and Watt's agent in Cornwall, Thomas Wilson, Weston wrote: "I hope we shall be able to avert that new blow aimed at us. I hope you will be able to discover how far Richard Trevithick has been concerned in erecting the Engines at Ding Dong & Poldice, & also how far he is connected with Bull".[10] This letter was dated June 22nd. A week later Weston wrote: "You said in one of your letters lately that Trevithick had got the engine (*i.e.* the one at Ding Dong) to work saying that he was not subject to or under the injunction to that effect: - if this can be sworn to, let it be done".[11]

A somewhat placatory letter was sent by William Carne to Thomas Wilson in Truro, stating: "In the Dispute between Ding Dong Advrs & Bolton & Watt - its not an Object worth Contending a Cort - for my Own Part I have no Objection to pay the Savings According to the duty the Engine is doing. Many More of the Adventurs is of my Opinion - at Present our Engine Shaft is on high Grounds at 3 strokes a Minute keeps the Waters - while we work under half the powers of the Engine of Course you will not Expect but half the Savings when Exceed that to be paid the whole".[12] Thomas Wilson replied the following day. As messrs. Rogers and Murdoch had been in the neighbourhood recently and had seen Mr Bolitho he had been expecting that the dispute between Boulton and Watt and the Ding Dong adventurers was to be resolved. Wilson's opinion was that no terms short of the full payment of the premium would be accepted: £10 17s 3d monthly, for the duration of the engine's use or until Boulton and Watt's patent expired, plus any costs incurred. He suggested that Carne should consider "whether, it will be more your Interest to accede to them, Stop the Mine, or run the risk of incurring the Chancellors displeasure by continuing to work on", even though Boulton and Watt "have not the least wish to Injure any Mine, but merely to defend their just rights, by using such means as the Laws of their Country will afford them".[13]

On July 10th Carne wrote to Wilson stating that the Ding Dong engine had been stopped.[14] The state of the mine appears to have been somewhat parlous: the cost book owed Carne £2,145 and the mine's costs had not been paid for the previous six months. Carne also stated that he had to build another engine, at a cost of £2,500, as the mine could not work another winter. The adventurers had reduced their dish (*i.e.* their dues, from 1/18th to 1/36th for two years or until the adventurers had realised £1,500 from the abatement.

In late September or early October 1795, Andrew Vivian and Richard Trevithick had met with Boulton and Watt to discuss terms, however no agreement was reached.[15] Trevithick had offered £800 for an engine he was building at Wheal Treasury, including arrears, and half premium for some other engines that he wanted to build elsewhere. In a letter from James Watt senior to Thomas Wilson dated October 5th the situation had been outlined. Vivian and Trevithick had "talked much of the good performance of T's engine at Dingdong which they say does 13 million pr bushel & that ours of the same size do not do above. This we cannot entirely credit. We are not sorry to be off with T. as we do not like him to interfere with Mr M. (presumably William Murdoch) whom we should however have taken care of in some other way, when such interference was likely to be hurtful, in the present case he could not have been affected as the engines were already undertaken by T. on his own account he being to find Engines, men, & coals for a monthly sum.[16]

A further demonstration of Weston's enmity towards Trevithick is shown in a letter dated 17 November 1795 which states "Trevithick must be personally served with the Injunction, cost what it will. A few Guineas to the officer will make this certain".[17]

Ironically, in 1796 there was an attempt by Thomas Gundry, by then the mine captain at Ding Dong, to try to get Boulton and Watt to employ Trevithick as one of their erectors. He wrote:

I have taken the liberty to trouble you with this by desire of Richd

Trevithick, Jnr., who have for some time past been employed by Edwd. Bull in mechanism. He desires not to continue in opposition to you, and is ready to give up everything in this county, and be under your direction. If you should employ him, you will certainly find him possessive of good abilitys in mechanics, natural as well as acquired, and is of an honest and peaceable disposition, he would be glad to serve either in Cornwall or Soho, the latter place in particular. If this step is taken I think the opposition in Cornwall would to a great measure subside. I would esteem it a particular favour if you would take the matter into consideration and don't doubt but that any favour conferred will be gratefully acknowledged by him, as well as, yr. mo. obedt. Servt. Thos. Gundry.[18]

Gundry was apparently held in some esteem by Boulton and Watt who, presumably, gave his request some consideration but William Murdoch appears to have been against the idea and Trevithick was never employed. It appears that the following year Boulton and Watt had relented, realising the advantages in employing Trevithick, but the latter then, perversely, refused the terms offered.

Failing to prove that Bull and Trevithick were partners, Boulton and Watt took out a separate injunction against Trevithick. This was recounted in 1868 by James Bolitho junior from recollections of his father (James senior, the former engine driver) who had worked all his life at Ding Dong. The latter recalled that "the engine had not been working long before [the agents of] Boulton and Watt came to the mine with an injunction printed out, and pasted it up on the door of the engine-house and upon the heaps of mine-stuff and nobody dared to touch them. But Captain Trevithick did not care, and he, along with Bull and the engineer William West, came and turned the cylinder upside-down right over the pump-rods in the shaft; they took off the cylinder top (it was the cylinder bottom before they turned it upside-down); water and oil used to be on top of the piston to keep it tight".[19]

Weston also stated that "at the time of the modification of the engine, Trevithick had erected a 'wind engine' which at times went so fast that they could not stop it, and some sailors came from Penzance and made a plan for reefing the sails". It is likely, however, that this refers to the "patent wind engine" erected at Wheal Malkin by Benjamin Heame in 1787, although it is possible that a second was erected at Ding Dong, in which Heame was also an adventurer.

Heame's death in 1789 may have curtailed any plans to build more of these wind engines. In this case it would seem probable that Trevithick was merely improving an earlier design, rather than devising his own, another example of his tinkerings. The description of Trevithick's wind engine spinning so fast suggests that his plan was merely to make it turn as quickly as it could; Heame's patent was specifically to prevent a quickly turning windmill from over-pumping or over-winding and thus to prevent accidents. Bearing in mind the ferocious correspondence that he was having with Boulton and Watt at this time it is also possible that he was seriously trying to find an alternative for steam.

According to Richard Trevithick's son and (somewhat biased) biographer, Francis, the conversion of the pumping engine took place in 1797. He wrote that the engine was converted into an open top cylinder, without beam or parallel motion.[20] The year was more or less confirmed by a Mrs Dennis who, in 1869, was living in Penzance and was then in her eighties. The following extract is taken from Francis Trevithick's biography of his father who wrote:

> Mrs. Dennis recollected Mr Trevithick at Ding Dong about 1797, fixing his new plan of pumps there, and at Wheal Malkin and Wheal Providence, adjoining mines. Her parents lived at Madron near these mines, and for two or three weeks Mr Trevithick came frequently to superintend the work there, staying at their house a few days, or a week at a time. He was a great favourite, full of fun and good humour, and a good story teller. She had to be up at four in the morning to get Mr Trevithick's breakfast ready, and he never came back to the house again until dark. In the middle of the day a person came from the mines to fetch his dinner; he was never particular what it was. Sometimes when we were all sitting together talking, he would jump up, and before anyone had time to say a word, he was right away to the mine.[21]

But Trevithick, however amiable in his leisure moments, could be a formidable opponent as Boulton and Watt were soon to discover. When finally their legal advisors found out Trevithick's Christian name and proceeded with the injunction, they could not find a man brave enough to serve it on the 'Cornish giant' (allegedly 6 feet 2 inches tall in stockinged feet) who continued his construction work at Ding Dong, and threatened to throw anyone who tried to stop him down the engine shaft.[22] An account book in Trevithick's writing commences:

> 1797, to Ding Dong, for five week's attendance, at a guinea at week. Ditto, fixing a 7 inch pole case with new lift and wood wind bore.[23]

At the end of the previous year, after thwarting all attempts by Boulton and Watt's agents to deliver their injunction, Trevithick, along with Bull and Captain Andrew Vivian, appeared at Boulton and Watt's foundry at Smethwick. What the specific reason was for this visit is unknown. It may be that Trevithick went there as a spy at the request of the rebel Cornish adventurers with whom he was connected, but whatever his motive was, it was a colossal blunder in that it gave Boulton and Watt their long-awaited opportunity of serving him with the injunction, what followed being vividly described by Matthew Boulton who wrote:

> Trevithick and his friends were observed at a Publick House facing my manufactory and the injunction was delivered which he received with much surprise, particularly as he thought nobody knew him. He seemed much agitated and vexed: however he afterwards went with Bull and Andrew Vivian to dine with Simon (Simon Vivian, one of Boulton and Watt's engine erectors) at the foundry where he found our men firing of cannons and rejoicing our victory which took away his appetite from his dinner. Andrew was also admitted to the foundry and manufactory but not the others. It is rather curious that although ye injunction could not be served in Cornwall, T. should have run into the Lyons (lion's) mouth and afterwards go to dine with the man they had banished from Cornwall.[24]

Watt's assistant, John Southern, described what happened next: "Bull took his dinner quietly; but Trevithick walked backwards and forewards in the house like a madman, and firmly resisted all temptation to dinner; till the smell of a hot pye overcame his powers, upon which he set to and did pretty handsomely, but in such a manner as shewed him not quiet in mind".[25]

Although the injunction had finally been served it seemingly did little to

'Cap'n Dick at Ding Dong'. 1987 drawing by the late Clive Carter. The figure on the right holding a plan may be Ned Bull.

77

deter Trevithick and the dispute dragged on. His engine at Ding Dong was reported to be working well, according to a letter, dated October 5th, 1797, which also gave details of 'duty'. This was the term used in comparison of performance between one engine and another, and was computed from the number of pounds of water raised to the height of one foot per bushel of coal consumed.

The engine at Ding Dong was said to have a duty of 23 million against a Boulton and Watt engine of the same size which only gave 16 million. Not unnaturally this was denied by Boulton and Watt's agents.[26]

By early December Matthew Boulton was getting increasingly impatient with Trevithick, writing to Thomas Wilson on the 6th:

> Trevithick's conduct is such a medley composition that we shall not trouble ourselves to unravel it & it is of little significance whether we are to add to his other transgressions a conexion with Bull. . . . He must or ought to be sensible from the manner in which he concluded the negotiations at Soho (Boulton and Watt's foundry in Birmingham). When we parted he fully gave us to understand that rather than accede to our demands of 2/3rds premium he should continue to erect his atmospheric engines and most strenuously asserted that he could work them cheaper than ours under the terms required by us. You now have another instance of his duplicity that while he was making protestation of this tenor to us he had secretly resolved to convert the engine to our principle and which intention you see he has carried into effect in defiance of law & his solemn assurance to the contrary. It would be in vain to make any agreement with a man of his stamp without security in hand for its performance & we have therefore only one offer to make, viz. to pay the premium of Ding Dong and other engines where our principles are employed.[27]

It appears that Trevithick was now altering the Ding Dong engine to a double acting type, the principle of which was that it employed both strokes of the piston by admitting steam on both: sides, therefore enabling two sets of pump rods to be used. Watt had introduced this type in 1784 and his method of coupling the engine to the two sets of rods was either by using a pair of angle or cross-bobs at the mouth of the shaft to give the required upward and downward strokes, or by connecting a diagonal rod to the second set of pumps attached to the inner end of the beam.[28]

On December 16th Trevithick wrote to Wilson:

I have received your letter last night stating Mr Boulton and Watt's demand on my engines, as to Ding Dong saving, I have no objection to pay according to your statement of £800 for a 63 inch cylinder. Ding Dong is 28 inches which I believe gives a sum of about £150 which sum I would be bound to pay in monthly payment should the engine continue to work single which I believe will be but a very short time as every preparation is already of working double. Now if it is agreeable I will pay you the monthly sums stated until the engine is turned double which I expect will be in the course of two or three months and then enter into bonds for the remainder of the time for double the savings above stated.[29]

James Watt junior then asked Thomas Wilson to obtain proof of what alterations Trevithick had made on the Ding Dong engine, and on the 23rd of December he sent the following draft for Wilson to write in reply to Trevithick's letter of the 16th:

I have communicated your letter of the 16th to Messrs. Boulton and Watt, who desire me to say that all your preparations are made for converting the Ding Dong engine into a double acting one and that change will take place in the course of two or three months; they have calculated the premium upon the supposition of its working two months single; and the rest of the term double, which makes the whole sum £310. Per this sum, payable in monthly instalments they insist upon your having your bond before further alteration is made on the engine and I therefore request that you will appoint an early day for giving me the meeting for drawing it up. I am further desired by Messrs. Boulton and Watt to intimate to you that you are not to proceed to the erection of any other engine upon this principle until you have settled the terms with me according to the aforesaid rate & given your bond in each case for the amount. They therefore expect that before you proceed to contract with the mines to alter any engine, or erect anew any engine upon their principle, that you in each individual case, apply for their license. Boulton & Watt cannot enter into any circumstances attending this or that mine, they consider the license as granted to you and not to the mines, and it is your duty to secure yourself against the adventurers.[30]

Doubtless the tone of this letter did little to improve Trevithick's state of mind and Watt junior's instruction to Wilson, in January 1798, as to how Trevithick was to be treated, were expressed in a similar vein when he wrote:

We have your favour of the 30th and 31st ulto. and having considered the circumstances you mention to Trevithick's working single at Ding Dong for some time to come, we think upon the whole it will be best to make out a bond upon that supposition now, and have a fresh bond when it is intended to be made double. The lump sum for working is £158 which if convenient to Trevithick, may be paid at once and there will be no occasion for a bond. . . . As soon as the Ding Dong business is concluded, and we understand that a formal application is made by him for leave to work his engines upon our principle, we shall state the sum for which he is to give bond in which we shall make allowance for the time necessary to get them to work.[31]

Seemingly by the middle of the month Trevithick and Wilson had reached a settlement. Two years later, in 1800, the expiry of Watt's patent ended the Boulton and Watt monopoly and at last the Cornishmen were free to alter or adapt their engines without the threat of legal action.

This was also a period of transition for the mine itself. Following the Trevithick - Boulton and Watt dispute the former workings to the east, around the original Ding Dong bounds, were rapidly amalgamating, but at the same time Wheal Malkin, to the west, was in steady decline. Thus, as one mine faded out, another came into prominence.

Chapter 7 references
1. Barton, D. B., 1967. *History of Tin Mining and Smelting in Cornwall*, Bradford Barton Ltd., Truro, p41.
2. Barton, D. B., 1967. *The Cornish Beam Engine*. Bradford Barton Ltd., Truro.
3. Ibid. p19 and Rolt, L. T. C., 1964. *James Watt*, Arco Publishing Ltd., p29

4. Halliday, F. E., 1959. *A History of Cornwall*, Duckworth, London, pp274-5

5. Dickinson, H. W. and Jenkins, R. 1981. *James Watt and the Steam Engine*, Moorland Publishing.

6. Dickinson, H. W. and Rolt, L. T. C., 1934. Richard Trevithick, *The Engineer and the Man.* The University Press, and Rolt, L. T. C., 1964 *op. cit.* p.29

7. Boulton and Watt Letters (in Dickinson and Titley, *op.cit.*)

8. Dickinson and Rolt - *op. cit.* p.21

9. Cornwall Record Office document AD1583/8/27

10. Cornwall Record Office document AD1583/8/29

11. Cornwall Record Office document AD1583/8/37

12. Cornwall Record Office document AD1583/8/32

13. Cornwall Record Office document AD1583/8/34

14. Cornwall Record Office document AD1583/8/57

15. Cornwall Record Office document AD1583/8/57

16. Cornwall Record Office document AD1583/9/102

17. Cornwall Record Office document AD1583/8/86

18. Dickinson, H. W. and Jenkins, R. 1981. *James Watt and the Steam Engine*, Moorland Publishing.

19. Trevithick, F., 1872. *Life of Richard Trevithick: With an Account of His Inventions*, Volume 1. Spon, London.

20. Ibid

21. Ibid

22. Rowe, J., 1993. *Cornwall in the Age of the Industrial Revolution*, Cornish Hillside reprint, p.106

23. Trevithick, F., 1872 *op. cit.* p.67

24. Boulton and Watt papers, Cornwall Record Office: AD1583/9/102

25. Ibid. p.28

26. Boulton and Watt Letters 5th December, 1797 (in Dickinson and Titley op. cit.)

27. Ibid. M. Boulton to T. Weston 6th December 1797 (in Dickinson and Titley - op. cit.)

28. Barton, D. B., 1967. *The Cornish Beam Engine*. Bradford Barton Ltd., Truro, p30

29. Cornwall Record Office document AD1583/9/117, Boulton and Watt papers

30. Cornwall Record Office document AD1583/9/122, Boulton and Watt papers

31. Boulton and Watt letters (in Dickinson and Titley *op. cit.*)

Chapter 8

The nineteenth century: 1801-1850

The nineteenth century saw Ding Dong firmly established as the most important mine in the parishes of Madron and Gulval, although the process of amalgamation of the numerous small workings which collectively became known as Ding Dong Mine had been a gradual one. It has already been noted that by 1782 there were sixteen individual workings around Greenburrow, Boskednan and Tredinnick which were named in Moody's survey as 'The Boskednan and Tredinnick Bounds'.[1] By the close of the 18th century those to the west, comprising Wheal Pool (SW 432 352), Myne-an-Dawnes (SW 435 351), Huel-an-Teal (SW 434 346); Little Speedwell (SW 432 346), Huel Malkin (SW 435 343), Great Speedwell (SW 436 342), and Huel-an-Boys (SW 437 433) had amalgamated to form Wheal Malkin, described by Collins as being "a very old mine which lies to the west of Ding Dong". To the east lay the bounds of Venton Ego (SW 441 353), Huel-an-Grouse (SW 444 349), Ding Dong (SW 442 347), Huel-an-Drean (SW 444 347), Huel Minnor (SW 445 349) and Huel-an-Yate (SW 442 346).

By the second decade of the 19th century these had united under the name of Ding Dong Mine. Most of the above-named workings were in fact the original bounds depicted on Charles Moody's bounds survey map of 1782. That this all but obsolete system of bounding was still in existence at Ding Dong was revealed in September 1856 in an advertisement concerning the sale of shares in a number of tin bonds which included "1/3rd part of Ding Dong Bounds in Tredinnick and Boskednan Commons".[2] In 1871 there was reference to dues paid to Wheal Yet (Yate) bounders who had received just over 1/5th.

Ding Dong bounders, Wheal Malkin bounders and Wheal Boys were also

This image shows surface workings, lode back, but possibly including costean pits, on two lodes converging on Bolitho's Shaft. View from the east. The track in the foreground leads from Greenburrow, to the left. *Cornwall Historic Environment Services*

referred to and in 1876 Little Wheal Grouse and Tallow Hedge Bounds were mentioned. Ding Dong is known to have been active in the first decade of the 19th century, although on a smaller scale as in April 1807 shares in the mine, then described as adjoining Wheal Malkin and Wheal Providence, were advertised for sale.[3] Dines states that Ding Dong was working in 1808 and was worked continuously from 1814-1878.[4]

However, it has already been established that the mine was active in 1810, a year which had witnessed a brief boom in tin prices, but in the following year the value of metallic tin had fallen from £157 to £141 per ton and from all appearances, with the exception of Wheal Malkin, all other workings in the vicinity were suspended, including Ding Dong which, as has been noted, resumed activity in 1814. The depression in the prices of both tin and copper was very sudden, the reason given for the reduced price of tin being speculation by merchants on fresh trade following the end of the war against France.[5]

At this time it was still the usual practice for the adventurers in tin mines of any importance to receive their shares of the profits in black tin or in block (metallic) form, and it was equally common for almost any adventurer of significance to hold shares in one or more smelting houses. Failing this he would join forces on commission with the owners of one to produce and sell tin for him, with the metal either coined under his own name or that of the smelters. This was particularly the case in that the profits in the industry came from smelting rather than mining and from the refining of the tin rather than its production as ore. Ding Dong was a typical example of the extent of the smelters' interests in a tin mine.[6] In 1815 Messrs. Daubuz, of Carvedras (Truro) smelting house, held a 5-16th share in Ding Dong, Messrs. Batten of Trereife (Penzance) smelting house 4-16ths, and the Bolitho's of Chyandour (Penzance) smelting house 3/16th, the remaining 4-16ths being held by eight others.

The chief adventurer in Ding Dong had been the unfortunate Richard Oxnam, who had been a highly respected figure in West Cornwall. In 1810 he had held office as High Sheriff of the county but his speculations in tin, coupled with his extensive mining interests and his association with the ill-fated John Gundry – whom he may have tried to assist – brought him into financial difficulties by 1816. In 1817 he was declared bankrupt and subsequently imprisoned for debt. His half-shares in Wheal Reeth and other mines were taken up by James Halse of St Ives, whilst his mansion at Rosehill was sold

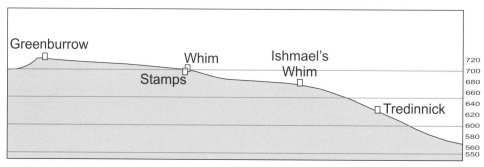

Cross section of Ding Dong, drawn along the track through the central portion of the sett, showing the elevation difference betweem east and west.
Heights in feet above sea level.

and his holding in Chyandour smelting house passed to his junior partners, largely the Bolitho family.

Two accidents, one each from Ding Dong and Wheal Malkin, were recorded from late 1815 or early 1816, both being caused by premature explosions of shot holes.[7] In the former, John Eddy was burned during the accident but recovered; in the latter Anthony Pocock had been "dreadfully burnt", resulting in total blindness. The information had been submitted by Mr Chenhalls and Mr Edward Collins Giddy. The latter was a surgeon while the other was presumably William Chenhalls of St Just. Chenhalls had devised a rod for tamping black powder made from a metal alloy which would not create sparks from friction against the rocks and had had them introduced into "all the Mines (in St Just) over which he had influence, or control". The improved tamping bar had been in use at Ding Dong for ten months by the time of publication.

Around the year 1819 the mine was visited by Dr John Forbes, who was then engaged upon the study of temperatures in numerous mines in West Cornwall, and later published a paper on the subject which was read to the Royal Geological Society of Cornwall in September 1819, and again in October 1820.[8] He described the mine as being about 400 feet above sea level and 606 feet in depth from surface, with 120 men employed underground. Forbes also gave a detailed account of the underground workings at that time in the following report: "Ding Dong, like Huel Neptune, consists of an old and shallower mine not now worked, conjoined with the part now worked, which is deeper. These two portions are united by means of a gallery at the depth of 50 or 60 fathoms under the surface. To the westward of this more distant part of the present Ding Dong there is still an older mine (Huel Malkin) adjoining, but not, I believe, actually communicating with the present mine, Huel Malkin has been entirely abandoned for many years".

This latter part of the statement may be incorrect as there is a hand-written notice, dated 24 June 1820, for the sale of "all the mine materials now lying at Wheal Malkin Tin Mine".[9] This included the 18- and 21-inch steam engines. Thus far, however, no advertisement has been seen in the various local newspapers, so it is not yet proven that the sale actually took place.

Forbes' reference to the eastern part of the mine as "then being worked", clearly indicates that the renewed working was centred around Tredinnick, and this is also borne out in his observation concerning the "declivity" (slope) of the ground and the fact that the 74 fathom level was, in reality, only 64 fathoms from surface in this part of the sett. Furthermore, Greenburrow engine house stands at over 700 feet above sea level while the Tredinnick engine house is about 100 feet lower.

During the great expansion in Cornish mining, in and after 1820, the most important metal was copper and consequently tin played no great part. Thus, by and large, what original records survive concerning the latter industry relate more to smelting than mining, with the exception of a few notable mines such as Wheal Vor and St Ives Consols. Most tin mines were small in size and great in number, and prior to the early 1850s detailed reports were very sparse apart from advertisements concerning the sale of shares or of the mines themselves. Ding Dong was not immune from this period of comparative obscurity and, apart from reports of accidents and sales of tin ore, little is known of the mine's progress and subsequent development during this early period.

In September 1820 it was revealed that the mine had been equipped with a new "fire engine" but the report did not specify the diameter of the cylinder,[10] and in 1825 a prehistoric stone circle at Tredinnick was reportedly demolished for building material.[11] What the reaction was to this piece of early 19th century vandalism history does not relate, but most likely the stone was used in the construction of an engine house, possibly the one at Ding Dong Shaft. This building housed a single acting 30-inch cylinder (6-foot stroke, equal beam[12]) pumping engine.

The early years were not devoid of tragedy. On the 14th of February 1827, five men were entombed by a fall of ground, only one of whom was dug out alive.[13] The men had been clearing a level through old workings at a depth of 30 to 40 fathoms from surface (lode unknown) when a "great mass" of debris and water fell on them; the fatalities were through drowning.[14]

In October 1829 the estate of Bosiliack was advertised for sale.[15] The notice gives mentions of two previously unknown tin mines, called Great and Little Bosiliack, possibly equating with Norden's "Tynn-worke called Basilsacke".

The mines were stated to have been worked for some years in "a very limited and confined manner", although even then profits of some hundreds of pounds per annum had been made. It was also stated that "a most respectable company of adventurers have recently applied for a sett or grant from the proprietor, and have agreed to work the mines on an extensive scale. From the improvements in machinery and the knowledge of mining generally since the old adventure ceased and was abandoned, there is every prospect of great and considerable profits to arise to the land from the dues."

Towards the end of the year a miner called William Hosken was killed in an accident at Ding Dong. He was 41 years old and was buried at Gulval Church, the burial being registered on 7th February 1830.[16] His son, Edward Saundry Hosken, born in 1826, started working at the mine as a blacksmith at the age of 8, just four years after his father's death.

In January 1830 it was reported that eight tons of black tin had been sold by Ding Dong, which was followed by a further sale of three tons, five hundredweights in October of the same year.[17] The mid-1830s were times of depression, but just how the mine was affected at this period is not known; interestingly none of the mines within the sett appear in the "list of the Copper and Tin Mines in the County of Cornwall, with the Names of the Mines and their Pursers" in Pigot's 1830 directory.

Various land sales from 1830 indicate that Ding Dong and Wheal Malkin were still working independently, one in February 1831 also mentioning Wheal Boys and one in July 1831 referring to a new steam engine (presumably a pump) and whim operating at Wheal Malkin.[18,19,20]

In July 1831 a miner by the name of Joseph Hoskins was killed by the premature detonation of a gunpowder charge in the Wheal Jacobine section.[21] Blasting accidents and rock falls were all too frequent, but accidents with gunpowder were sometimes the result of sheer carelessness. After a bore-hole had been drilled, a quantity of gunpowder was poured in and pressed home with a tamping bar. The latter was simply an iron bar which was sheathed with copper to prevent sparks from being struck by the action of iron grazing the sides of the hole, but in many cases a plain iron borer was used, often with tragic consequences.

87

An advertisement for the sale of Boswarthern in February 1834 gives what may be the last reference to Wheal Malkin;[22] the final amalgamation of the mines was about to take place. In April that year, John Hosking, aged 22, was charged with stealing a pair of flannel drawers belonging to a miner from Ding Dong called John Trembath. Hosking was sentenced by Samuel Borlase Esquire to one month's imprisonment with hard labour.[23]

By the end of 1834 Ding Dong had acquired another pumping engine, this with a 21½-inch cylinder. There were now four engines at work on the mine, two pumping and two winding, the latter 12-inch and 15-inch respectively, and in the following year the 30-inch engine was pumping from a depth of 88 fathoms (528 feet) and discharging an average of 39.87 gallons of water per minute.[24] It is unclear what happened to the Wheal Malkin engines; the pumping engine does not seem to have survived (as it is missing from the above list) but there are no clues as the fate of the whim; later references to the removal of engine parts from Greenburrow imply it was left on site.

The winter of 1836 was a particularly terrible one with severe gales from at least January to April 1837, with heavy snow in the latter month. In March the wind was described as "So tremendous a gale as we were visited with on Saturday night, was never remembered here".[25] This must have had a serious affect on surface work at the mine as well as affecting the supplies of Welsh coal, not just to West Penwith but to Cornwall. In addition, many ships were wrecked or lost around the local coast and many fishing boats were unable to put to sea in Newlyn and St Ives. In April the mayor of Penzance started a subscription for the relief of Newlyn, badly affected by the weather.[26,27] The weather was also responsible for the initiation of a plan to build a breakwater in Mounts Bay to protect the Penzance and Mounts Bay vessels (it was estimated that between 200 and 250 were sheltering from the gales),[28] but this was unsuccessful and the coastal trade had to wait a number of years before the harbour facilities at Penzance were extended.

A report on medical conditions in the Lands End area included one of Ding Dong's miners, a man called Trembath. This 50-year-old man had worked underground for nearly forty years, often in bad air, and had only recently been affected by his condition, dyspnoea. This condition, also known as shortness of breath or air hunger, is a debilitating symptom that is a common symptom of numerous medical disorders, particularly those involving the cardiovascular and respiratory systems.[29] In 1836 the mine was said to employ 200-300 persons, a very imprecise number from the Statistical Society of London.[30]

Another criminal case concerning Ding Dong was reported in March 1837.[31] This was another case of theft, and one Matthew Daniel was indicted for having "feloniously stolen from Ding Dong one Dutch frock and one pair of corduroy trowsers", the property of William Grose. Daniel was also charged with having previously stolen one woollen shirt, the property of William Andrews; he was acquitted of the first charge and found guilty of the second and sentenced to one month in prison with hard labour. Apparently incorrigible, in April 1839 Daniel (also spelled Daniell) was convicted of stealing another pair of trowsers, with a pair of drawers, both the property of Thomas Carnow of Morvah and Zennor Mine, to the north of Ding Dong.[32] Daniel was found guilty of the crime and, after a certificate of a former crime being shown to the court, was sentenced to fourteen years' transportation (the usual period for transportation was seven years[33]). The constable of Morvah, Walter Gendell, gave such a "blundering statement of his share of the business" that he was asked by the learned Judge if "they chose constables in Morvah for their stupidity".

Another blasting accident was recorded in May 1838 when a man called Phillip Richards was killed while working underground.[34] Richards left a wife and two children. In May 1840 the mine was reported as being "in the full course of working" which indicates the likelihood of a brief suspension of activity in the previous decade. The report also stated that there were now five engines on the mine, two pumping engines and two winding engines, the latest being a stamps engine driving 24 heads.[35]

The year 1840 was said to be a bad one for the mine in terms of accidents recorded, although whether more accidents actually occurred in that year is not known. In May a man called George Alexander, one of the mine's agents, was tending some machinery on the mine when he was struck on the back by part of it, at the same time losing a finger from his left hand.[36,37] He was put under the care of Alfred Berryman, the mine surgeon.

In October that year two men, William Rowe and William Trathan, both aged 19, were charged with having stolen "a quantity of ores, the property of John Batten and others, adventurers".[38] Witness for the prosecution was Thomas Trembath, a miner working at the 30-fathom level near where the two defendants also worked. On the day that the theft took place Trembath had come up from underground between 2 and 3pm; the two prisoners were working the afternoon core to the east of where Trembath and his comrades had been working. The tin ore which had been extracted had been left in the level, some pieces of which were of particular appearance; the following day they were missing and were found where Rowe and Trathan had left their ore pile. Captain Edward Treglown (presumably one of the mine's agents, but this was not stated in the article) stated that the prisoners had confessed against each other, that Trathan had said that Rowe had asked him to assist in taking the stuff, which he did. Treglown gave Trathan an excellent character but, despite this, the two were sentenced to three months' imprisonment with hard labour.

Yet more criminal activity was recorded at the mine in October 1840.[39] Charles

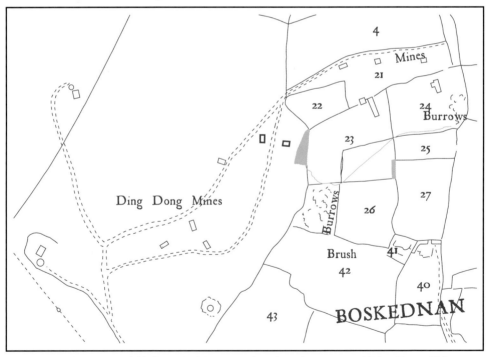

Extract from the 1842 Gulval tithe map showing the extent of Ding Dong Mine.

Phillips was charged with stealing a pair of trousers belonging to John Jacka of Ding Dong. The accuser had noticed his trousers missing on June 10th, and on going to Towednack he found the defendant with the trousers on him. Charles Phillips, the defendant's father, was called on his behalf. He swore that his son, who also worked at Ding Dong, had put on Jacka's trousers in error while changing his clothes and left his own in their place.

When questioned, Jacka said he did not find any trousers left at the mine in lieu of his own. Phillips was found guilty of the crime and was sentenced to three months' imprisonment with hard labour. On November 24th a miner called Richard Jennings was killed after being "buried by a great mass of rubbish" that fell on him; he was buried so deeply that it took over two hours to extricate his body.[40]

1840 was a crisis year for Cornish mining, for both copper and tin. Both metals were either sold by public ticketing or by private treaty with the smelters and there has been much debate regarding the relationship between the mines and the smelters, most of which is beyond the scope of this book. However it is a matter of record that the great majority of tin miners and streamers got together to form a committee to come to a private arrangement with just two smelting houses, Fermin de Tastet & Co. and Vigurs, Batten, James & Co.[41] It is interesting to note that even with the Penzance smelters Bolitho's holding a large number of the shares in Ding Dong, it was unable to join in with this clique. Only five or six mines did not join and the principal tin producers, Charlestown United Mines and Polgooth, were managed by John Taylor, who could see no great benefit from the new arrangement.

In 1842 a total of 328 persons were employed at the mine, comprising 301 male and 27 female workers. Of those employed underground there were included four boys under the age of 15, the youngest being between 11 and 12 years old, viz:[42]

Age	Surface	Underground
9-10	3	-
10-11	2	-
11-12	6	1

12-13	5	-
13-14	3	1
14-15	8	2

The total adult male workforce at that time amounted to 250.

In 1815 the mine had been in 16 shares and by 1843 this had increased to 32 shares;[43] by 1844 the number had increased to 672 of which Batten & Sons owned at least 46, these being advertised for sale.[44] As 672 is a multiple of 32 the increase in share numbers may just be a simple division. In October 1849 the list of shareholders given in the cost book (the earliest remaining for the mine) shows the dominant position of Thomas Bolitho and Sons:[45]

Name	Location	Shares
Messrs. Thomas Bolitho & Sons	Chyandour	222
Messrs. R. V. & H. Davy	Penzance	60
Miss Mary Batten	Penzance	46
Rev. Thomas Leah & Ed. Leah	St Keynes & Penzance	42
Samuel Prodwell	Penzance	41
John Richards	Penzance	34
Messrs Gill & Co	Tavistock	21
William Cock	Penzance	21
Samuel Higgs	Penzance	20
Thomas Coulson	Penzance	20
Messrs E. & H. Davy	Penzance	15
Henry Mathews	Penzance	10
Nicholas Holman	St Just	10
Richard Lanyon	Kennall Vale	10
Rev. Henry Batten	Penzance	9
Thomas Neame	Penzance	8
John Roscorla	Penzance	6
Richard Wellington	Penzance	4
Richard James	Penzance	3
John Foster	Penzance	3

Christopher B. Foster	London	3
Samuel Phillips	Penzance	2
James Nicholas	Penzance	2

The list is interesting for two reasons. Firstly, it shows the dominance of local people holding shares; one of the foreign shareholders was from a local family (the Leahs) while the others were mostly traders. The rest of the 'foreign' adventurers held a total of only 24 out of the 672 shares. Secondly, the list shows a number of individuals and companies with mining-related interests. These include the Davys (mining interests), Miss Mary Batten (presumably a member of the smelting family), Gill & Co. (engineers), Samuel Higgs (involved in numerous local mines), Thomas Coulson (merchant), E. & H. Davy (merchants), Nicholas Holman (engineering), Richard Lanyon (gunpowder) and Richard Wellington (the mine's purser). Edward Leah was to became one of the mine's surgeons in June 1850, joining Arthur and

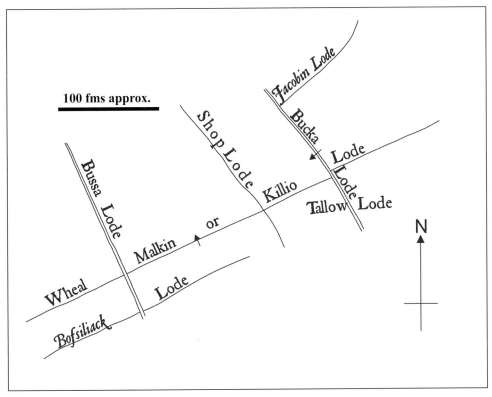

The lodes at Ding Dong Mine in 1843.

Thomas Berryman, their duties to be shared equally.

The mineral lords at this time were:

Name	Amount of dues
Duke of Leeds	£8 16s 11d
Mr Batten	£10 8s 4d
Mrs Agar	£5 4s 3d
Mr Levy	£1 18s 8d
D. E. Stevens	£1 18s 8d
Miss Mathews	£1 1s 3d
George Jennings	£1 1s 3d
Mr Ellis	£1 1s 3d
Capt. Treglown	7s 10d

While the Duke of Leeds did not have the largest shareholding he was listed above his social inferiors. The agents at this time were John Truran (formerly at Wheal Trewavas, near Helston), salary nine guineas per month, Richard Bone, £5 per month and Henry Nicholas, £2 10s per month. James Bolitho appears to have been the senior engineman at £2 7s 6d per month with nine others and two pitmen. "Patent frames" were in use on dressing floors, possibly a reference to Borlase's buddles. Twenty four men were employed underground and fifty two "at stamps" *i.e.* on the dressing floors.

Through the mid 1840s there were notices of numerous share transfers, one example being in January 1845 when 10-672 shares were transferred from William Birch to Richard Vinnicombe and Huphry Davy, and in November of the same year another nine shares were acquired by the same gentlemen from the Reverend Henry Batten.[46] During this period the mine was said to be "making good dividends".[47]

In 1846 a number of mine representatives (agents, pursers and shareholders) met to set up the Mining Property Protection Society.[48] The mines included Ding Dong along with several St Just mines and several St Ives mines as well as North United Mines which, like Ding Dong, was somewhere between the two mining districts. The Society was to be set up for the purpose of "taking

94

the produce of the tin mines to the markets, that no leavings or other tin of any kind should in future be at the disposal of any other workmen". Once the Society was properly formed the smelters would be informed that they could not lawfully take tin from anyone other than officially from the shareholders.

John Batten was appointed chairman. There seems to have been a large trade in illegal tin at this point and Batten stated that: He could not, of course, say to what extent the plunder prevailed, but he knew that within twelve months £400 worth of tin had been disposed of by one individual having a stamps, and he had no doubt that the tin had been stolen from Ding Dong Mine although there was no legal proof.

It is not known what, if anything, became of this Society. At the meeting, held in Penzance, the purser of Great Wheal Vor was "diffident" about joining as a similar organisation would probably be formed in that area.

During the year the workings had begun to extend west and in December the agent's report stated that a winze was now being sunk below the 25 fathom level on Cluekey (Klucky) Lode in the West Killiow section, and also Bosworthen adit level was being driven west.[49] In Bolitho Shaft the 30-fathom level was being driven west on Captain Afters Lode as was the 45-fathom level. In the bottom of the 50-fathom level, at the crossing of the Jacobine and Standard Lodes, a winze was being sunk, and driving on the 60-fathom level north, on New Flat-rod Shaft, was now under way. At Bolitho Shaft the 60-fathom level was being driven to intersect the Slide and Bucca Lodes.

In the 80-fathom level a cross-cut had been driven on Slide and Wig Lodes, and at the 50-fathom level a drive west on Standard Lode was in progress. In addition, at South Killiow Shaft, the 45 fathom level was being driven west on Malkin Lode.

In November 1849 a 12 year old boy called J. Orchard had his frock caught up in some of the machinery; he was thrown to the ground, an arm severely fractured and his face cut. Luckily his frock gave way before he was even more seriously injured. He was taken to his father's home in Madron churchtown, where medical aid was in attendance; he was said to be in a precarious state.[50]

In this year the mine had ten engine drivers: James Bolitho, William Bone, Henry James, Richard Tregloan, William Stevens, William Jenkin, Edward Tregloan, Nicholas Thomas, Samuel Bastian and William Walker.[51] The cost book also indicates just how much a family affair it was to work for Ding Dong Mine. While the Bone family was over-represented amongst the engine drivers, another four members of the family worked on the dressing floors. The Cock and Peak families had five members each, four Tregloans and Riches and three each for Bastian and Polglaze. At this time some 54 persons were employed on the dressing floors, of which 16 were females.

The following figures, taken from the *Mining Journal*, shows the share values and total capital from 1851-76.

Date	Value	Total
1851	£5 0s	£3,360 0s
1856 (1.3)	£32 0s	£21,504 0s
1857 (5.12)	£32 15s	£22,008 0s
1858 (6.3)	£33 15s	£22,680 0s
1858 (4.9)	£33 5s	£22,344 0s
1859 (23.7)	£36 17s	£24,763 4s
1859 (3.9)	£37 14s	£25,334 8s
1861 (22.6)	£39 2s 6d	£26,292 0s
1862 (14.6)	£40 18s 6d	£27,501 12s
1863 (18.10)	£43 11s 6d	£29,282 8s
1863 (12.12)	£44 10s 6d	£29,926 16s
1865 (18.11)	£48 14s 6d	£32,743 4s
1866 (29.12)	£49 14s 6d	£32,619 12s
1876 (12.2)	£50 11s 6d	£33,177 4s
1876 (3.6)	£51 9s 6d	£33,767 12s

NB The figures in brackets are the dates of the weekly issues of the *Mining Journal* from which these figures are taken.

By 1850 the number of workers had dropped considerably. There were then about 100 men employed, half of which were tributers and the remainder on tutwork.[52] The decade ended with a fatal accident: in September, E. Kitto was struck by a stone falling down the shaft "by which he was so dreadfully crushed, that he expired in an hour".[53] Meanwhile at Greenburrow Shaft the disused engine was being repaired and the shaft cleared; pumps had been acquired from Wheal Vor near Breage.[54]

Chapter 8 References

1. Courtney Library document B/16/1: Tin Bounds of the parishes of Madron, Gulval, Zennor, St Just, Ludgvan, Towednack, Sancreed, Paul, Morvah and Sennen, 1782; Charles Moody Collection, Royal Institution of Cornwall, Truro

2. *Royal Cornwall Gazette* 26.9.1856

3. *Royal Cornwall Gazette* 4.4.1807

4. Dines, H. G., 1956, *The Metalliferous Mining Region of Southwest England.* HMSO, London.

62. Jenkin, A. K. H., 1951. *News from Cornwall.* Westaway Books, London.

5. Barton, D. B., 1967. *A History of Tin Mining and Smelting in Cornwall*, Bradford Barton Ltd., Truro, pp26 and 47

6. Paris, J. A., 1917. *On the Accidents which occur in the Mines of Cornwall* [etc.]. T. Vigurs, Penzance.

7. *Transactions of The Royal Geological Society of Cornwall*, vol. 2 pp181-2 (see reference 29 below for more on John Forbes).

8. Cornwall Record Office document STA/717/1

9. *Royal Cornwall Gazette*, 9.9.1820

10. Kenneth Brown implies that this was for the Tredinnick house but the cost books confirm that this was one of the last to be built (see below).

11. Lean, T., 1835. *On the Steam Engines in Cornwall*, Simkin, Marshall & Co., London.

12. *Royal Cornwall Gazette* 17.2.1827

13. *Cornish Telegraph* 10.4.1867

14. http://hosken.net/William%20Hosken%201789.htm

15. *West Briton* 16.10.1829

16. *Royal Cornwall Gazette* 6.2.1830 and 16.10.1830

17. *West Briton* 13.8.1830

18. *West Briton* 25.2.1831

19. *West Briton* 29.7.1831

20. *Royal Cornwall Gazette* 8.7.1831

21. *West Briton* 7.2.1834

22. *West Briton* 11.4.1834

23. Lean, T., 1835., *op. cit.* tables 4 and 9 pp143-5

24. *West Briton* 1.4.1836

25. *West Briton* 8.4.1836

26. *West Briton* 29.4.1836

27. *West Briton*6.5.1836

28. Forbes, J. and Conolly, J. (eds), 1836. A sketch of the medical topography of the hundred of Penwith comprising the district of Landsend in Cornwall. In: *British and Foreign Medical Review.*

    John Forbes was in Penzance during the early part of his career. He was responsible for bringing the use of the stethoscope into British medicine from France, having translated all of the original French documents on the topic. He was also the first Secretary of the Royal Geological Society of Cornwall. At the end of his career he was a Fellow of the Royal Society and held the position of Royal Physician.

29. Edmunds, R., junior, 1836. A Statistical Account of the Parish of Madron, containing the Borough of Penzance in Cornwall. In: *Journal of the Statistical Society of London*, Volume 2, Charles Knight & Co, London.

30. *West Briton* 31.3.1837

31. *West Briton* 5.4.1839

32. Ironically it was mining that stopped transportation to Australia. Gold was discovered in New South Wales in the 1850s, then later in Victoria. Australia thus rapidly became a destination of opportunity, rather than an open prison. Until 1868 some convicts were still being sent to Western Australia however gold was also found there, in similar quantities to that found elsewhere. The largest gold nugget ever found was the 'Welcome Stranger', described as a tolerably heavy load for two men': it weighed 71kg. The London Chartered Bank advanced the pair £9,000 for the nugget and later paid tem a further £381. The two finders were John Deason and Richard Oates, the former from Scilly and the latter from Pendeen, just a couple of kilometres to the west of Ding Dong.

33. *Royal Cornwall Gazette* 4.5.1838

34. *Penzance Gazette* 20.5.1840

35. *Penzance Gazette* 20.5.1840

36. *Penzance Gazette* 5.11.1845

37. *West Briton* 30.10.1840

38. *Penzance Gazette* 9.12.1840

39. *Mining Journal* 30.5.1840 and 6.6.1840; there is almost weekly correspondence on this topic.

40. Parliamentary Papers - Children's Employment Commission - report by Charles Barham Esq.

41. *Penzance Gazette* 15.3.1843

42. *Penzance Gazette* 13.11.1844

43. Cornwall Record Office document RG101: Cost book

44. Cornwall Record Office document DDX 745: Cost Book extract - Brooke Index

45. *Royal Cornwall Gazette* 22.5.1840

46. *Penzance Gazette* 22.7.1846

47. *West Briton* 30.10.1840

48. *Mining Journal* 10.11.1849

49. Cornwall Record Office document RG108: Cost book

50. Cornwall Record Office document DDX 237/11

51. Cornwall Record Office document RG93: Cost book

52. *Mining Journal* 7.9.1850

53. Information per Alasdair Neill

Chapter 9

The Nineteenth Century: 1851-1880

In January 1851 work was taking place on a number of lodes, mostly in the central to western part of the sett.[1] These included Captain After's Lode at Bolitho and West Killiow shafts, Clukey Lode, New Lode east of Flat Rod Shaft, Standard Lode east of Graham's Shaft and the Boswarthen adit on Standard Lode. In June that year Edward Leah was appointed surgeon "jointly in thirds" with Arthur Berryman and Thomas Berryman "it being considered that whatever arrangement the surgeons may make among themselves each must consider himself bound whenever called upon to do so in case of accident or any emergency".[2] Leah was a shareholder in the mine and it may be that his appointment was achieved because of this, a not uncommon event in Cornish mining. In November the same lodes were being worked. One interesting point to note is the mention of Greenburrow Shaft being divided and cased, with a footway (ladders) being put in. This dividing was to enable the ladderway to be enclosed in its own compartment, safely away from the pump rods; other reports mention a capstan at the shaft and it is likely that it had been used primarily for winding but was now also being used for access and egress.

By the early 1850s the eastern workings were beginning to show sign of exhaustion as was revealed in June 1851 when Captain Matthew White, of Marazion, declared that the eastern portion of the sett was now looking very poor and suggested transferring operations to the lode which ran through the Venton Ego section, the latter lying immediately north of the current workings. On the financial side the accounts showed a loss of £51 2s 6d on the previous three months' working.[3]

The balance sheet[4] showed that the debit had occurred fairly suddenly since

September 1851 despite the fact that no great change had taken place in the price of tin. No information is given in the cost book regarding extra costs and it is presumed that the debit account was caused by a reduction in the amount of tin produced, at a slightly lower average price.

Quarter to	Credit	Debit	Price range/ton
Dec 1849	307		42-51
Mar 1850	326		37-51
Jun 1850	509		33-53
Sept 1850	355		35-53
Dec 1850	79		42-56
Mar 1851	26		39-54
Jun 1851		206	33-50

A number of accidents were recorded in the early 1850s. In May 1851, Josiah Richards, working as a kibble-filler, was taking rods (probably drill rods) at the 60 fathom level when he was suddenly struck by a large amount of rubbish.[5] Richards was struck on the back or side of the head, causing blood to flow copiously from his ears. Although assistance was rendered immediately he was lying in a "precarious state" at the time of the report and his recovery was regarded as hopeless. He was aged 27 and had a wife and two children dependent on him for support. In March 1852 two more men, J. Hocking and J. Humphries, were killed by another collapse.[6]

It is difficult to assess how many of these accidents were the result of the state of the shafts or pure bad luck. In a report by Captain Matthew White in June 1852, recommending that Greenpease Shaft be sunk to the 50 fathom level he stated that the shaft was "bad for drawing, and only can be used within a degree of safety to a 50 or 60 fm level".[7]

Following the presentation of the March 1852 report in June, it was resolved that an agent be called to inspect certain parts of the mine regarding its future working.[8] To this end a meeting was to be held at the Mounts Bay Commercial Bank (*i.e.* at Bolitho's offices at Chyandour) "to determine best method of further and more vigorous prosecution of the workings". The loss on three months working had been £471 2s 5d, to offset which a call of £1 per share

DING DONG MINE.

SIR,—Considering the antiquity of this mine, and the large amount of dividends it has yielded to the shareholders, it seems remarkable that so little has been said about it in your Journal. Until of late, even the name, I believe, did not appear in your List. This silence may fairly be attributed to the fact that the shareholders were few in number, rich in purse, and liked the dividends too well to invite other people to come in to share with them. I am not aware that the dividends have been so large at one time, or in one year, as in some mines that might be named; but the same having extended over hundreds of years, the aggregate thereof probably equals the best mine in the county. The last dividend was 2352*l*., on three months' tin, being 70s. per 1-672d share. The tin sold in the last quarter realised 4832*l*. 16s., while the total expenditure was 2391*l*. 2s. 6d. only. Of late this mine has come a little more under the notice of capitalists, who are glad to purchase shares at the current price, which is considered under their real value, and will probably soon range considerably higher. A majority of the shares is held, I find, by the rich firm of Bolitho and Sons, of Chyandour, tin smelters; and Mr. T. S. Bolitho, of that firm, is the purser. This mine has been worked for generations—so long ago that there are no records of its origin, and, from its present state and indications, will probably survive the present and next generation. It is situate in Gulval, about four miles north of Penzance.

Camborne, March 12. —— ONE UNCONCERNED.

Plaintive letter regarding the lack of information on Ding Dong Mine:
Mining Journal 15.3.1856.

was called. At the subsequent meeting on June 22nd it was resolved that an additional underground agent be appointed, the selection being to be left to Messrs Bolitho.

In March 1853 Captain John Truran had been engaged in 'dialling' (surveying) and was talking to some miners near a shaft when a mass of rubbish, which included one stone of about a ton in weight, fell away, catching two men and taking them five fathoms down the shaft.[9] One of them, called Carbis, was completely buried by the material and only extricated with great difficulty. Another miner, called Cock, from Madron, fell onto the rock and fractured both bones of one leg.

The account for September 1854, held in December, gave grim reading.[10] Losses since June 1853 had almost been constant, £131 4s 9d in that month, £148 17s 9d in September, £65 3s 9d in March 1854, £308 10s in June and £247 9s 9d in September. With a profit in December 1853 the loss over the period, and the present deficit, was £902 16s 9d. To meet the loss a call of 30s per share was made, equal to £1,008.

In December 1854, it was disclosed that the deeper levels had been unproductive for many years and furthermore there had been no great profits made from the workings below the 60-fathom level. Consequently it was resolved to abandon the deeper levels in order to confine the task of pumping to one engine, the 21½-inch, thereby keeping the 30-inch as a standby. Unfortunately there are no indications as to the locations of these engines, although the 30-inch was probably on Ding Dong Engine Shaft. However, there was a respite in the mine's fortunes by the middle of the decade. In 1851, tin prices had begun to rise and by the following year the price of metallic tin stood at £92 per ton, reaching £120 per ton in 1855.[11]

In March 1856 the mine declared a dividend of £3 10s per share which was followed by another in September of £2 10s and in December of £1 10s.[12] In March that year a correspondent writing in the *Mining Journal* had remarked that the mine "maintained a cautious silence which was attributed to the fact that the shareholders were few in number, rich in purse, and like the dividends too well to invite other people to come in to share with them".[13] In fact the situation became even better, as the following table shows:

Quarter	Profit	Dividend	Bolitho's share
December 1854	£72 0s 10d		
March 1855	£270 14s 5d		
June 1855	£732 4s 3d		
September 1855	£1,065 4s 5d	£3 10s	£777
December 1855	£2,461 19s 4d	£3	£666
March 1856	£2,431 14s 0d	£3	£666
June 1856	£1,527 12s 4d	£2 10s	£555
September 1856	£1,250 18s 7d	£1 10s	£333
December 1856	£876 3s 5d		
Total dividend	£10,688 11s 7d	£13 10s	£2,997

NB the dates of the dividends relate to the quarters in which they authorised, not necessarily when they were paid.

In September 1856, and over four years after the decision to appoint, a new agent was finally taken on. This was Matthew Daniel, whose father had been an agent at the mine up to the time of his death; his salary was six guineas per month. It is also possible that this was the same youth who had been sentenced to transportation for stealing 'trowsers' in March 1837; this date, some months prior to his appearance at the mine, would have been shortly after the expiry of his sentence.

The accounts for March 1857 showed a credit balance of £1,882 8s 4d and a dividend of £1 per share was declared. At this time it was decided to erect a new pumping engine, a 40-inch, on North Killiow Shaft and shortly afterwards an engine was purchased from Messrs. Harvey and Co. of Hayle for £705.[14] The exact location of North Killiow Shaft is not known - it is not near East, West and South Killiow Shafts, however the mine plans show an Engine Shaft to the east of the dressing floors and this seems a likely location; it also ties in with Ding Dong Engine Shaft. In addition there is what appears to be a pond, possibly for the boilers and condenser, to the north.

Three months later, at the beginning of June, the accounts revealed a balance of £1,210 8s 4d on the amount of ore sold which, when added to the sum of £3 11s in sundry credits, yielded £3,929 7s 4d against a total on the three months from January to March of £2,318 1s 4d, leaving a credit balance of £1,611 6s and a profit of £402 17s 8d on three months working. Concerning the lodes, Captains John Truran and Matthew Daniel reported that since the last meeting, in March, underground operations had been progressing steadily but the quantity and quality of the tin ground had not improved, adding that the returns for the quarter ending June 30th would not be equal to those of the previous quarter, and that the principal falling-off was below the 50-fathom level on White Lode. About 120 men were employed at this period, 89 of whom were on tutwork at £3 4s 3d per month, and 31 were tributers at £3 10s 4d.[15] September saw a loss of £183 9s on the previous three months' working.[16]

During the previous month, one of the Ding Dong miners, with his two sons, all tributers, had been working "out of core" at Wheal Conquer and Wheal Lady, in the Towednack area.[17] Sinking on a north-south crosscourse they cut a lode 12-18 inches wide in virgin ground, worth 8s to 34s per bushel. Neither mine had worked for several years and had amalgamated, but without reworking.

A fatal accident occurred at the mine at the beginning of November 1857 when

The Tredinnick engine house from the south west. *Tony Clarke.*

The Tredinnick engine house from the north west. *Tony Clarke.*

The interior of the Tredinnick engine house; cylinder loadings nearest camera, plug door in the bob wall in the background.

Ishmael's whim from the north. The boiler house was formerly attached on this side.

The interior of Ishmael's whim showing the cataract pit in front of the cylinder loadings, plug door (upper part of bob wall) and access to cataracts (bottom of bob wall).

Ishmael's Shaft and Ishmael's whim seen from the west.

**Possible engine pond opposite the location of the North Killiow and
Ding Dong engine houses.**

**The remains of the tramway joining Ishmael's engine house (in background) and the
dressing floors.**

The dressing floors, all but inaccessible. The remains of the stamps engine house lie beneath the vegetation in the left middleground, buddles to the right.

Masonry near the base of the stamps: possible catch pits.

Greenburrow engine house atop its burrow.

Hold-down bolts for the 40-inch engine in the Greenburrow engine house. The presence of these bolts demonstrates that the engine was scrapped.

Greenburrow Engine Shaft and the balance bob pit.

Greenburrow Engine Shaft viewed through the grille.

111

"Of all the dismal dreary places":
Greenburrow engine house photographed in August 2007.

Photograph showing damage being done to the dumps at Greenburrow by off-road
cyclists. The shaft capstan was formerly situated at far right of image, behind the deep
groove.

Bolitho's Shaft.

Line of shafts and shallow workings on Bussa Lode;
tips at Greenburrow in the foreground.

Lode back workings and shallow shafts to the north of Greenburrow.

Shaft at the base of the bob wall of the East Ding Dong engine house.

114

The overgrown remains of the East Ding Dong engine house.

South Ding Dong with Ishmael's whim on the horizon. The masonry in the foreground may be part of the engine house.

The new headstone for Eliza Jane Hall,
dedicated on 12 July 2013 (see pp148-149).

a twelve year old boy named Tobias Boaden of Ludgvan fell ten fathoms from a ladderway in one of the shafts. The boy fell into the water at the bottom of the shaft, where he drowned before he could be rescued.[18]

In December 1857 the accounts showed that the expenses for the previous three months totalled £3,3128 14s 10d which, against a credit balance of £1,429 17s plus £1,601 14s on tin sold, resulted in a balance of £97 3s 10d against the mine, and a call of 15s per share was made. Captains Truran and Daniel reported that at Greenpease Shaft the underground operations in the different levels had continued much as usual, but with a slight falling off. In Bosiliack they had passed through clay and had found ore producing ground in the area of the Ding Dong Lode about 100 fathoms from the known workings, declaring that this area had long been considered as being rich in tin, and several previous attempts had been made to work it without effect.[19] Ding Dong Lode was presumably worked over a long period although it was hardly ever mentioned by name.

The lode runs from Bolitho Shaft, north-north-east of the Greenburrow engine house, east through the centre of the sett past the north end of the dressing floors and on to Ishmael's Shaft.[20] The lode seems to have been particularly rich at its intersections with other lodes, of which there were several: Bucka, Wig and Slide as well as several structures which appear to be crosscourses.

Work on the new engine house and other locations had taken place during the last part of the year, apparently in an attempt to completely alter the pumping and winding arrangements about the mine.[21] In July the Ding Dong engine was being repaired by James Bolitho while work had started on the new engine house to the south; stone was being raised and lime (for mortar) had been brought in from Penzance. In August the road, presumably a farm track, was being repaired to give access to the new engine house site. In September the balance bob pit at the Greenburrow capstan was being cleared while in October the balance bob pit at North Killiow Shaft was being cleared, the headframe was being built and the engine erected.

It is interesting to note references at this time to "taking out and bringing down boilers from Green Burrow &c"; implying that a steam engine of some sort, possibly a whim, had been built there but was now disused. It is unclear if

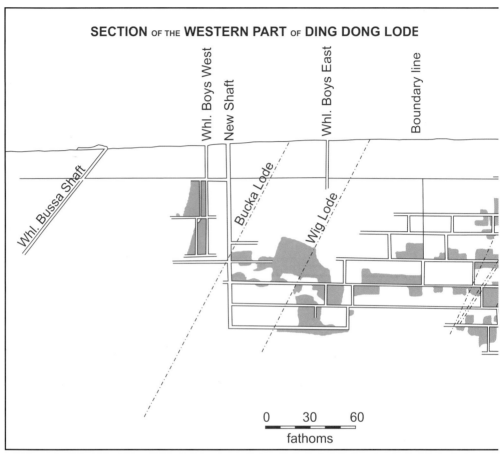

SECTION OF THE WESTERN PART OF DING DONG LODE

Whl. Boys West
New Shaft
Whl. Boys East
Boundary line
Whl. Bussa Shaft
Bucka Lode
Wig Lode

0   30   60
fathoms

the word 'capstan' refers to a shaft capstan, for raising and lowering materials in the shaft, or to a winding engine. The movement of the boilers appears to have been a major task involving a number of groups of men as shown in the cost book for November 1857:

> William Pengelly & co Taking out boilers and assisting
> Pitman at Sump Shaft
> Building hedge for pool at Killiow
> Richard Pengelly & co assisting to bring down boilers at Green Burrow
> James Maddern & co assisting to bring down boilers at Green Burrow

In addition, John Green and company were at Killiow Engine Shaft, assisting the engineer to put in the new engine. In December a balance bob pit was

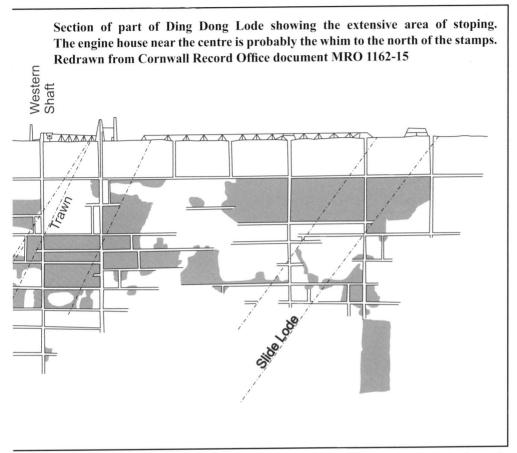

Section of part of Ding Dong Lode showing the extensive area of stoping. The engine house near the centre is probably the whim to the north of the stamps. Redrawn from Cornwall Record Office document MRO 1162-15

Western Shaft

Trawn

Slide Lode

being built at Greenpease Shaft and pump rods fixed in the shaft, rods (presumably flat rods to operate the pump rods) were being brought from Ventonego Common to Greenpease Shaft while at Greenburrow Engine Shaft a number of people were helping to take up rods. This latter is slightly perplexing as it implies that pumping was being or had been carried out at the shaft; possibly this, too, was carried out using flat-rods from one of the other pumping engines.

A rather curious case of tin stealing was recorded at the mine in December 1854.[22] William Stevens, a farmer, was attracted by his dog to a certain spot in a croft near the mine, where he discovered a sack of tin ore hidden under a furze bush. Stevens immediately reported this to the mine's agents and a watch was set. Between midnight and 1am that same night, two men, riding donkeys, were seen about twenty yards from where the sack was hidden.

The two passed the spot and tied the two donkeys to a gate about thirty yards away. Captain Bennetts immediately sent for more assistance, and upon their arrival, he ran to the stamps floor, thinking the men might be there. On opening the door into the shed, be heard a noise as if someone was there, and called out telling them to stand, or he would shoot them! Immediately he heard the sound as of a shovel being thrown down, and saw "two objects resembling men ran out of the shed". He then went into the engine house and called to the engineman to look out, when he was informed that two men had gone by the door, running towards the croft in the direction of the spot where the donkeys were left tied to the gate.

Bennetts followed on, and on coming up to where the donkeys were, he found two men called Matthew Stevens and Thomas Trathan in the custody of Captain Daniels and William Pengelly. They were taken to the account house, and given into the custody of a constable, after which Captain Bennetts and Captain Daniels proceeded to the stamps floor, where they found two sacks nearly full of tin ore, one sack exactly corresponding with the one that was found in the croft. The prisoners were taken before the magistrate, D. P. le Grice, and remanded in custody so that the police and the adventurers might have an opportunity of obtaining further evidence. On Wednesday December 10th a great many witnesses were examined and their depositions taken. Trathan, of Morvah, and Stephens, of St. Just, were then committed to trial at the Quarter Sessions at Bodmin.

Early in February 1858 the mine was said to have shown an improvement and it was stated that shares were in constant demand at £17 10s to £18 10s, having previously stood at £43 to £44 before the drop in the price of tin.[23] However, in March the accounts showed a balance of £693 5s 9d against the mine and a call of £1 per share was made.[24] About this time a total of 206 men and boys were employed, the average age, according to a report in the *West Briton*, being twenty-six years and one month. "But", it continued, "if we take only such men as are actually engaged below, the age sinks to twenty-four. The two youngest are eight, much too young, and the oldest, seventy-four, who is employed as a dry man at surface".[25]

Throughout the first half of 1858 Ding Dong Engine Shaft was being stripped of materials, suggesting that it was being abandoned. Skips were being installed at Killiow Engine Shaft in June, indicating that it was being used for winding as well as pumping. The adverse balance continued through the year, being £673 5s 9d in December 1857, £341 6s 2d in March 1858, £1096 3s 8d in June, £866 17s 11d in September and £432 14s 6d in December. It is likely that the work on reorganising the mine was responsible for reduced output, however the patchy nature of the tin and the fluctuating price both acted adversely. Calls were made in December (£1), June (£1 10s), September (£1 10s) and December (12s 6d). By the latter month a total of £120 was owed in unpaid calls. The old Ding Dong engine was still at least partly in place as the boiler was being stripped of steam pipes.

In the latter part of 1859 work started to concentrate on Standard Lode, to the south of the new Engine Shaft.[26] The lode was being worked between the 20- and 50-fathom levels and from a number of shafts, including Croft Reeth and Greenpease Shafts. Work was also being carried out on Malkin Lode while the erection of a horse whim and "takle" (tackle) on Qualk Shaft indicates another centre of operations.

In October 1859 there were reports of an improvement in the 50-fathom level on Standard Lode, east of Greenpease Shaft.[27] Here the level was being driven by three men at £4 per fathom, the 20-fathom level, west of Greenpease Shaft on White Lode, by three men at £1 per fathom, and the 40-fathom level east of Greenpease Shaft by three men at £6 per fathom. The end in the 30-fathom level, on Malkin Standard Lode east of Greenpease Shaft, was reported to be looking poor and, at present, was being driven by four men at £6 per fathom.

The 30-fathom level on Little Kluky Lode, east of Greenpease Shaft, was being driven by four men at £5 per fathom and three men were driving east of Killiow Shaft, on Standard Lode, at £5 per fathom. The engine shaft (North Killiow Shaft) was now down to the 60-fathom level, where it was reported that further sinking was about to be resumed.

The lode in the 60-fathom level, east of the shaft, was said to be poor but good stones of tin had been found in the 40-fathom level east of Tregear Shaft (not mentioned by Dines), which was being driven by four men at £4 per fathom. There were, at this time, 35 men on tutwork on the different lodes and 40 on tribute at prices varying from 4s to 18s in the £1. The agents' report concluded

DING DONG MINE,

Penzance, 27th Nov., 1869.

Sir,

A Meeting of Shareholders in Ding Dong Mine will be held at the Office, Chyandour, on Tuesday, the 7th December, at Two o'clock, *for the purpose of auditing the Accounts*, and transacting other business.

I am, Sir,

Your obedient servant,

R. WELLINGTON,

Shares.   Purser.

In the event of any change of address, it is requested that notice thereof should be at once sent to the Purser.
No Transfer will be registered between the 3rd and the 8th December.

Notice calling a meeting of shareholers, taken from the 1859 cost book.

by remarking that the mine was just about paying costs.

In December 1859 a fatal accident occurred when a worker, named Thomas Madron, while carrying out a repair to the stamps, slipped and fell onto the axle which was in motion at the time. The unfortunate man was instantly carried round and sustained such extensive injuries that they caused his immediate death.[28]

In March 1860 the cost book gives references to: Samuel Olds and company stems [shifts] taking abroad Greenburrow engine Various people clearing and loading stone Francis Bone & co sundry stems assisting L. Luke abroad Greenburrow and Wheal Boys engines The engine at Greenburrow is presumably the one referred to as having boilers removed in 1857. The Wheal Boys engine could also refer to Greenburrow as that shaft is within the old Wheal Boys bounds so the mention of both names is strange and would appear to imply that two different engines were being worked on. In February the decision was made "to thoroughly repair whim engine and the work to be done with least delay" and this work may have been carried out to find spare or re-usable parts. This probably refers to the engine formerly situated just to the north of the dressing floors.

In May, James Jelbert and company were helping to erect the new steam whim cage (the winding drum), Thomas Ellis and company worked sundry stems repairing and cleaning the steam whim boiler, John Nicholls and company assisted in taking down the old whim cage and put up the new axle and cage and William Polglaze and company assisted in clearing the boiler house and whim pool (presumably the reservoir for the boiler water). The whim boiler was covered in June. In the quarterly account there is a payment to Nicholas Holman and Sons (of the St Just Foundry) for £100 for a "new 18-inch cylinder, nozzles, etc. to steam whim as per contract", indicating that the engine was almost completely rebuilt.

The *UK Mineral Statistics* for the year ending September 30th 1860 shows that the mine sold just over 80 tons 13 cwt of concentrate for £6,722 14s 6d. In March 1861 it was reported that during the previous quarter Ding Dong had sold tin to the value of £1,087 10s, there being a loss on three months working of £652 0s 2d.[29] The net balance against adventurers now stood at £960 19s 14d. At the previous meeting there were thought to have been grounds to look for increased returns however, although the monthly sampling had improved, it was not up to expectations. In the light of the finances a call of £1 8s 6d per share was made. In light of the poor report, the agents were instructed to carefully examine all the workings and present their results at a special meeting to be held on April 4th.

In April and May work was being carried out at the 60-fathom level at Qualk Shaft, on Jilbert's, Ellis and, probably, on Qualk Lode. Work to build an arch, for unknown purposes but possibly support, commenced at Tredinnick Shaft in June and the shaft was collared the following month. The burrow at Hard Shaft was cleared in July and pulley stands were put up so that the shaft could be used for winding.

In October that year a description of the mine was given by Captain John Nancarrow of St Ives Consols.[30] He stated that the lodes in the mine had been wrought from a very remote period and for the last 100 years without intermission, during which time it gave large profits to the adventurers and it was not long since it gave within two years a profit of £12,000. The ground had been worked almost throughout the length and breadth of the sett and its deepest part towards the east the workings extended to 115 fathoms below adit, which was about 15 fathoms deep. However, the workings there were said to be not very extensive, and for some time the water had not been below the 70-fathom level (where it was at that time). The machinery, erected near the middle of the sett, consisted of a 40-inch pumping engine, a 24-inch stamps engine and a 17-inch whim engine, regarded as being ample for working the mine. Presumably the 17-inch whim represents the 18-inch engine mentioned in the accounts for June. There is no mention of the 30-inch engine, probably on Ding Dong Shaft; presumably this was disused by this time and its parts recycled (see below).

The operations were on five lodes. Ellis's Lode, bearing 30 degrees east of north, crossed Gilbert's a little north of Rowe's with which the latter was thought probably to join to the southwest. All of the ground opened on this lode was 18 fathoms in length and not then extensively stoped, however, 40 tons of tin (tin ore, probably meaning rough concentrate) had been raised there. Although the ground was hard the backs (the ground above the working level) were working at an average tribute of 4s in £1; the bottom was worth £25 per fathom at the then price of tin. The lode was very rich in the north especially in the lower part. This was regarded as an important discovery; the lode was whole above and below (*i.e.* had not been previously worked), the tin making strongly towards the north may indicate the near approach to another lode. Were another lode to be intersected then a further improvement might be expected. The mine appeared to be a permanent one, containing as it did a vast amount of unwrought ground, and its advantages many. The water was easy (*i.e.* there was not very much to be pumped), the cost of the machinery light, the ground required but little timber and the tin was of excellent quality.

The December quarterly account, however, showed a different story. The loss on the three months' working was £652 0s 2d, leaving a balance against the adventurers of £960 19s 4d, and a call of £1 8s 6d per share (worth £957 12s) was made. The agents reported that "the mine continues poor, with no immediate prospect of a change". It was then resolved that the agents should examine all of the workings very carefully and prepare a special report to be laid before a meeting of the adventurers on Thursday April 4 at Bolitho & Sons offices at Chyandour. At the meeting the agents' report (which was not recorded) was adopted. Essentially this was that the parts of the mine which appeared to be important should be "pressed forward with all speed with as many men as can profitably be employed". The 60-fathom level, possibly on Jilbert's Lode, was to be cleared up east to Tredinnick Shaft. Here it was thought probable the "new lode" would cross that level; if discovered there Tredinnick would be the most advantageous shaft for working it. It did not appear that a reduction could be made in the number of men employed but that the additional number of men required for working the new lode could be taken from such parts of the workings at Greenpease, as they could be best spared. The agents were urged "to be particular in observing economy, and making such reductions on the effectual working of the mine".

During the month Providence Shaft was being cleared above adit (having been collared in October and November). The shaft was shallow, only down to the adit, and appears to have been abandoned, or at least neglected, for some time. The surface around the shaft was being cleared and a shaft tackle was being raised preparatory to sinking the shaft.

During 1861 the mine's prospects had actually improved through an increase in the amount of tin sold during the middle part of the year. In the March quarter it had been just under 14 tons but had increased to 33½ tons in June, was just under 31 tons in September but had reduced to just over 16 tons in December.

Work at Providence Shaft commenced in earnest in January 1862. In addition, Jilbert's Lode was being driven north on the 50- and 60-fathom levels to come under the line of the shaft. In February, William Hosking and company were being paid 200 shillings per fathom to sink Providence Shaft below adit, the adit also being cleared north of the shaft; by May this had increased to 240 shillings, suggesting that this was very hard work indeed. In June the 10 fathom level was reached, in July a skip road and ladders were put in from surface to the shaft bottom and in August sinking recommenced; in October the miners were being paid 360s per fathom. The shaft appears to have reached the 20-fathom level by December.

On October 20th, during a severe storm, the stack of the pumping engine house – the 40-inch – was struck by lightning and toppled to the ground.[31] The falling masonry partially damaged the engine-house but the boiler house was completely demolished. Fortunately no-one was present except the engine man who escaped without injury.

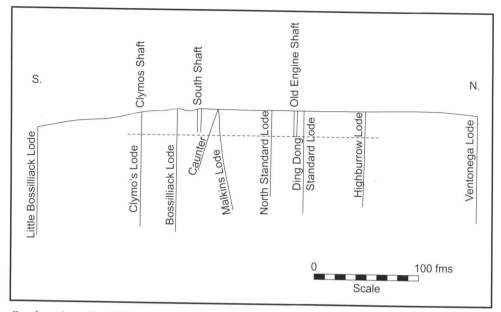

Section along Good Fortune Lode shpwing numerous lode intersections. The amount of stoping is not known but this lode was one of the earliest to be worked, as demonstrated by the outcrop workings to the west of the Greenburrow engine house. Redrawn from Cornwall Record Office document MRO 1162

During the year, work in the mine was concentrated on two sites, Qualk and Tallow shafts. Work was carried out on Tallow Lode (between the 40- and 50-fathom levels), Bucka Lode (the 25 and 50 fathom levels) and Jilbert's (50 and 60 fathom levels), with minor work in other parts of the mine.

Despite developing these areas the actual tin mining was largely carried out by the tutworkers, presumably in an effort to cut costs. The mine usually had around 17 tribute pitches operating but by October 1862 this had dropped to one. In November there were nine but the total would not reach normal levels until mid-1863. Tin production reached a low of 9¾ tons in March 1862 and had only increased to 15½ tons by December. A large amount of repair work to the various adits, levels and shafts was carried out during the year and this routine maintenance was an unwelcome cost to the adventurers. The work was essential, however, as blocked adits and levels impeded drainage while shafts in poor condition were dangerous as well as inefficient.

It should be borne in mind just how extensive the workings within the sett were. Clymo's Shaft lies approximately 1300m south-west of Providence

Shaft while the workings extend approximately 600m at right-angles to this axis on twenty different lodes. The lodes were worked at this time to a depth of 60 fathoms below adit from twenty seven shafts. In November and December the roofs of the Killiow engine and boiler houses and the stamps engine house also needed repairing.

The account for December 1862 showed a loss on three months of £666 5s 4d, giving an adverse balance of £707 2s 7d. Unpaid calls amounted to £351 3s 6d, comprising arrears of £208 3s 4d and £143 owed from the last call (£1 per share in September). Tin sales were 15 tons 10 cwt 2 qtrs 4 lb for £68 per ton, which realised £1,054 5s 4d. The adventurers appear to have been very concerned about the running of the mine at this point and a committee "to inspect into the state of the present agencies in the mine, and to make such arrangements as they may think necessary" was appointed, comprising Thomas Bolitho & Sons, James B. Coulson, Benjamin Andrew, Richard. V. Davy, Edmund Davy, Samuel Higgs and William Douglas.

A special meeting was held at Chyandour on January 19th 1863 where it was reported that the loss on the coming quarter would be about £676. Currently the unpaid calls amounted to £525 which it was hoped would "reduce" to about £100. A number of letters from various shareholders were read giving their opinions as to the future of the mine; there appears to have been a suggestion to sell it. On being questioned, the agents stated that the materials were worth about £2,400. It was resolved that, until the tin ground in the bottom of the 60-fathom level on Qualk Lode had been further explored, it would not be prudent to come to any definite conclusion and that the subject be deferred till the quarterly account meeting in March.

During the month Providence Shaft was sinking below the 20-fathom level at 340s per fathom. In February the 50-fathom level on Jilbert's Lode had been extended under the line of the shaft and was being sunk at 140s per fathom and the following month the shaft was being sunk below the 60-fathom level at 180s per fathom.

In April a meeting was held at the offices of the Mounts Bay Commercial Bank, presumably at the instigation of the committee of adventurers, at which the decision was made to appoint a new managing agent. Coming to

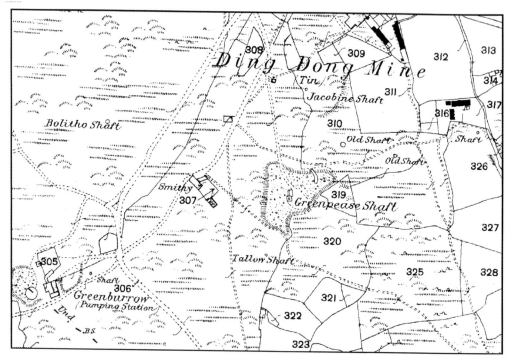

The western part of Ding Dong Mine from Greenburrow to just south of the dressing floors. 1st series 25-inch OS map.

a conclusion, the minutes state that "we do not for a moment call in question the zeal or ability of Captn J Truran, nothing but the continued ill health of Captn M Daniel throwing heavier duties on the manager (who from increasing years is understandably less able to go underground than formerly) induces us to make a change". It was decided to offer the job to Captain Francis Bennetts at a salary of nine guineas per month and that John Truran be offered a "situation" at five guineas per month "with the understanding that he should devote all his time and energies in attending to the surface work, keeping the accounts and also in assisting the manager by his advice on the underground workings". Bennetts' appointment was confirmed in May (at the March account meeting) and the decision was also taken to appoint an additional agent at six guineas per month. At the same meeting J. S. Bolitho resigned his position of purser, partly as he had not acted in the post for some years, and recommended the appointment of Richard Wellington in his place, the latter apparently having stood in for Bolitho "for many years".

Bennetts finally assumed his post in June 1863; Matthew Daniels' salary had been increased from six to seven guineas per month. In this month work reached a frantic pace at Providence Shaft, which was being sunk below the 30-fathom level (at 300 shillings per fathom), below the 50-fathom level (at 200s) and below the 60-fathom level (at 260s). In addition it was being raised over the 50-fathom level (at 280s) and above the 60-fathom level (at 180s). During the earlier part of the year the numbers of tribute pitches and tutwork were reduced, reflected in the sale of just under twelve tons of black tin in June, although this sold for the comparatively healthy price of £70 per ton. There was more bad news at the meeting held in Bolitho's offices at Chyandour on December 1st 1863.[32] The three months' operations had cost £1,668, tin sold was 15 tons 9 cwt at £68 per ton, and the loss on the quarter had been £617 16s 6d. Another call, of 19s per share, was made to clear the balance. Providence Shaft was complete for drawing at the 70-fathom level, that level now being driven east (towards Ishmael's Shaft) to get under the

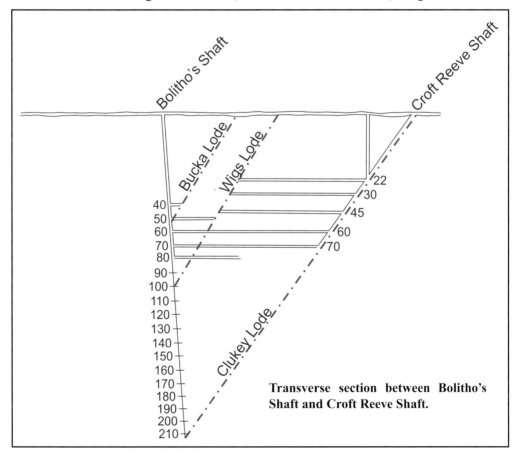

Transverse section between Bolitho's Shaft and Croft Reeve Shaft.

tin ground worked on the 60-fathom level. The 70-fathom level west had another 6 fathoms to drive to reach the tin ground in the 60-fathom level, and was driving at 110s per fathom. The bottom of the 60-fathom level was being cleared, presumably in preparation for stoping. The 50- and 30-fathom levels were being driven east, but nothing had been met with.

In the "Greenpease district" they were driving the 60-fathom level east on New South Standard Lode to prove the ground below the 30- 40- and 50-fathom levels where rich bunches of tinstone were yielded some years before.

The areas being worked were:

Tallow Shaft
40 west on Bucka Lode at the shaft
40 west on Tallow Lode at the shaft
40 on Bucka Lode west of shaft
50 on Tallow Lode west of shaft

Greenpease Shaft
30 on White Lode at the shaft
50 on New South Standard Lode west of shaft
60 on New South Standard Lode west of shaft

Croft Reeth Shaft
20 west on Alex Lode west of shaft
40 on Malking Standard Lode west of shaft
20 on Clukey Lode at the shaft
20 on Wig Lode west of shaft

Providence Shaft
30 east of on Jilbert's Lode (securing and fixing skip road in this lode)
50 on Jilbert's Lode east of shaft
50 on Rowe's Lode at the shaft
70 west and east on Jilbert's Lode at the shaft

In December, Ding Dong Engine Shaft was being re-collared, and William Hosking and company were preparing to take out the Ding Dong engine.[33] It is remarkable, with all the work that had previously been carried out removing parts, that any were left, although it could possibly have been re-erected and not noted in the cost book. The December account revealed a loss on three months of £776 9s 5d, resulting in a balance against the adventurers of £874 17s 3d, to clear which a call of £1 6s per share (equal to £873 12s) was made to be paid at once. A report by Francis Bennetts was discussed and it was resolved that the suggestions given should be adopted, although the plan to erect an engine to drain the eastern (Tredinnick) part of the mine would be deferred for the present. The plans contemplated (though not given as they were not part of the mine's costs) would involve a considerably outlay, not less than a call of £1 per share for the next six or eight quarters. It was hoped that any shareholders not wishing to contribute to the costs would relinquish their shares immediately as some of those present were willing to buy them based on Francis Bennetts' valuation, minus any cost incurred up to the time of sale or relinquishments. As a result, 89½ shares were relinquished, seventeen bought by Bolitho, eight each by the two Davys and three for Francis Bennetts, all at £2 each.

The latest plans for the mine involved the re-use of Ding Dong Engine Shaft as a winding shaft; the skip road was fixed and repaired and tackle fixed in February, when the boiler was removed, and the shaft was being secured from surface to adit in March. In April and May the foundations for a new pumping engine house at Greenburrow were being cleared. This was a labour-intensive operation involving three groups of tributers: John Maddern and company, Thomas Bolitho and company and Henry Tregloan and company. The shaft was being cut down and divided from surface and being secured in the Bucka Lode; ladders were being fixed from surface to adit. During this year, Thomas Spargo records that the workforce consisted of 89 men, 20 women and 12 boys, a total of 121 persons.[34] Spargo also stated that the mine was not making returns in excess of costs at that time.

In May 1864 yet another accident was recorded, this one through blasting.[35] On Friday the 20th, Michael Trembath, about 16 years of age, had been working as a tributer in the back of the 40-fathom level west of the shaft on Tallow Lode. Thomas Bolitho, who had worked as a tributer for many years in the same mine, had a pitch in the bottom of the same level at a short distance from Trembath; the latter worked there alone and had commenced his contract only a week earlier. During the morning Trembath spoke with Bolitho several times. About noon Bolitho asked Trembath, as he tamped a hole, if he was nearly 'in course'. He said he was, and he did not think it would 'heave the burthen'. Bolitho then went away but heard, more quickly than expected, a report and at the same instant a scream. He hastened towards Trembath's pitch, and found the young miner lying on his face and unable to speak. He lifted him against the side of the level and went for help; he returned two minutes with Phillip Maddern. Trembath was then not quite dead but he was insensible, and on being removed to the nearby shaft expired. Several severe injuries to his breast, chest, and head had caused his death.

The charging practice at Ding Dong was to compress the powder with a wooden rod or charging stick, and to tamp with an iron rod. This was given in evidence by Captain Francis Bennetts, who had been an agent for 14 months. The Coroner, Captain Bennetts, and several of the jury members (including many miners, one of whom had been severely injured by a premature explosion), discussed the problem of how to avoid similar accidents and what regulations could be enforced in mines. The jury returned a verdict of accidental death, unaccompanied by any recommendations.

Work on Ding Dong Engine Shaft and what was then called Greenburrow Engine Shaft continued through June. An interesting item in the cost book is for Thomas Bolitho and companions (no immediate connection with the smelting and banking company but possibly related) who were clearing and securing Good Fortune adit as well as drawing water from the 70-fathom level at Providence Shaft, working at both ends of the sett. At the June quarterly account meeting (held on September 13th) it was resolved that an engine of 24 or 36 inch cylinder "be at once provided to drain the Providence and Tredinnick shafts and to draw the stuff". This was a quick turn-around from the December 1864 meeting, possibly caused by concern over the continuing losses; that on the previous quarter have been £592 8s 3d. So far £250 had been spent on the new engine house at Greenburrow. The costs for the engine house were given in the August 1864 account (part of the quarter ending September, meeting held in December):

Henry Roach and co:

Building engine house and boiler house at Green Burrow	£151 8s 9d
Roofing do.	£10 16s 0d
Building brickwork on stack	£2 5s 0d
Do. walls of lobby	£2 14s 9d
Taking down scaffolding	£2 15s 0d
Supplying and fixing granite on bob wall	£2 5s 0d
Putting in boilers	£9 0s 0d
Total	£181 4s 6d

Subsist £140-0-0, Materials £29-4-4, Doctor 45/-, Club 30/-

Balance	£41 4s 6d

The central part of the mine was being abandoned at this time and in September the Killiow pumping engine was moved to Greenburrow Shaft by Henry Richards, "as per contract £8". Thomas Spargo records that the 30-inch pumping engine was idle during the year but there is no information regarding its condition.[36] The number of people employed comprised 89 men, 20 females and 12 boys. Spargo confirms that the mine was not doing as well as it could:

At present this mine is not making returns in excess of the cost. This, however, is a common occurrence in mines that must have been opened in the early ages – a period of which we hold few records. From the many chances of success in such a labyrinth of underground workings, it would be unwise to distrust Ding Dong, for not doubt it will renew its power of profit, and the establishment now so old will be continued onwards in the course of time, if not with brilliant with generous or moderate success.

In October John Eustice was employed erecting the Killiow engine at Greenburrow. In December, Elisha Marks and company (some of the mine's masons) were building the balance bob loading and pit at Greenburrow and plastering and whitewashing the inside of the engine house as well as building the coal yard. The coal for the engine was then brought from the mine's coalyard to Greenburrow. At the December account meeting the agents were "instructed to press forward the erection of the second engine in the expectation that before the end of June the tin ground now under water at Providence will be drained as well as at the western ground." The extra equipment was thought likely to cost £1,000 but it was hoped that tin production would increase as a result. The *UK Mineral Statistics* show that in the year ending December 31st the mine produced just over 62¼ tons of concentrate which sold for £3,923 7s 6d.

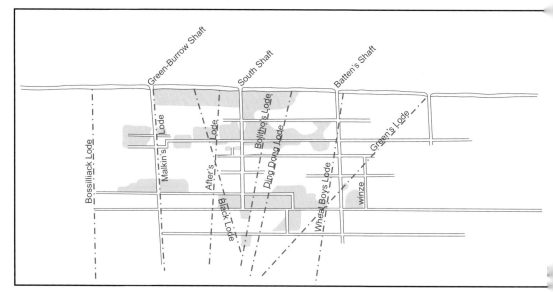

Section showing the large number of lodes intersecting Bussa Lode.
Redrawn from Cornwall Record Office document MRO 1162-7

Work on the foundations at Tredinnick commenced in January 1865 and the erection of the engine house commenced in March, the work being carried out by Elisha Marks and company. In mid January the mine was reported as "recently very much improved".[37] According to the reporter of the *Cornish Telegraph* the mine was, "perhaps, the oldest and one of the richest mines in Cornwall, the success of which it may be stated, has been the foundation of an immense fortune to a very deserving family of bankers and tin-smelters, &c., in Cornwall." An engine had recently been moved to another part of the mine, suggesting that the new house at Tredinnick was made from the masonry of the one at North Killiow Shaft. In the development of this new part some good discoveries of tin had already been made, at the Providence Shaft in the 70-fathom level. The price of the shares had improved from a few shillings to £12 each.

During this quarter much work was carried out to the principal shafts: Tredinnick, Ding Dong Engine Shaft and Greenburrow Engine Shaft. The Tredinnick engine house was still being built in April although there is a note that the engine was being watched in May, suggesting that it was in operation. In that month flat rods were fixed from Greenburrow Engine Shaft to Ding Dong Engine Shaft; presumably these were fixed to the balance bob of the former and connected to an angle bob at surface at the latter.

With all of the work being carried out on the mine the account for June 1865 was the worst in the mine's history. The loss on three months had been £1,577 16s 5d, leaving an adverse balance of £2,823 1s 5d. Tin sold had been a miserable 8¾ tons at the very low price of £51 15s per ton; this had realised just £456 13s. Sandys Vivian and Co. had been paid £155 4s for a new boiler and another engineering bill was for £91 19s 1d, paid to N. Holman & Sons of St Just. To meet the loss a call of £4 4s per share was made; £1 10s to be paid before 15 September, £1 10s before December 1st and the remaining £1 4s on or before February 1st 1866, with the understanding that a 2½% discount shall be allowed on any of the calls that were paid before due. The cost of the new engine house was given in the August account:

<u>August 1865</u>

Elisha Marks and company by building engine and boiler house at Tredinnick	£105 7s 6d
Roofing of above	£6 19s 6d
Putting in boiler complete	£4 10s 0d
Building brickwork on top of stack	£2 15s 0d
Striking scaffolding, weatherboarding, etc	£2 15s 0d
Sundry work repairing roofs and stopping beam holes in engine house	£1 12s 6d
Building walls and sump house	£1 16s 0d
Building bob stand at Tredinnick	£3 6s 8d
Building bob pit at providence	£4 6s 8d
Building Ding Dong bob pit and stand	£5 10s 8d
Providing clay for building bottom flue of boiler	£0 5s 0d
Total	£139 4s 6d

The June call did its job and in September a balance of £87 8s 6d in favour of the mine was reported, helped by the sale of 33½ tons of black tin, although the price was still low, £58 10s per ton. The mine had actually produced a profit on three months of £88 1s 11d.

According to Spargo, the mineral output for the year 1865 was 50 tons 5 cwts., 3 qrs., 9 lbs. which sold for £3,302 17s,[38] but these figures contradict other sources, namely the *Mining Journal* which gave the output and value for that year as 83 tons 1qr., 9 lbs., realising the sum of £4,815.[39]

By the mid 1860s the price of tin had dropped again.[40] In 1863 black tin stood at £64 per ton, but in 1865 the price had fallen to £55 and dropped even further in the following year to £48 per ton. The cause of the 1861-65 collapse in the price of tin was the American Civil War.

In November 1865 the following letter appeared in the *Mining Journal*:[41] I have been advised to purchase shares in this mine, but cannot ascertain the parties under whose management it is placed, or find any reports in the Journal by which I can learn of its position or prospects, - will anyone state where the offices are, who is the purser etc.

This inquiry, innocent enough, resulted in an exchange of ill-tempered correspondence. A Mr J. Williams, of Penzance gave a somewhat acidic reply the following week when he wrote:[42]

> In reply to 'Investor' in last week's journal, the purser of Ding Dong is Mr Richard Wellington, of Chyandour, Penzance. The last call was made in September and amounted to £4 4s per share, and in about a fortnight there will be another call. With £3,000 per quarter expenditure it is feared the managers will be a long while before they make a dividend. Indeed, it is anticipated to take all the tin which may be raised from Providence Shaft to pay for the other workings.

This letter was challenged in the following week's issue of the *Mining Journal* when another correspondent stated that the expenditure from January to March had been £1,688 9s 11d and for the quarter ending June 30th, £2,034 9s 5d.[43] He concluded: "I will leave 'Investor' to form his own estimate of the

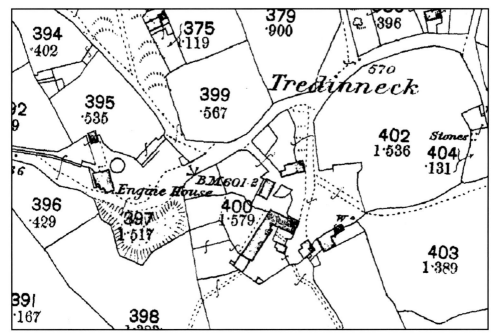

Part of the 1st series 25-inch OS map showing the Tredinnick engine house and the end of the tramway to the dressing floors. The circular feature to the right of the house is probably a shaft capstan. The shaft itself is some distance to the north of the house.

value of the predictions, as well as facts set forth by J. Williams". In between these exchanges the *Cornish Telegraph* was still able to say that "from recent reports we are glad to be able to state the mine is still improving".[44] The following month the *Cornish Telegraph* was still being optimistic, stating that the share price had improved to £16 17s.[45] Parts of the mine were valued at £2 10s to £3 per fathom although these do not seem to be particularly high values. According to the report the most important area was that around Providence Shaft.

In December 1865 Captain John Nancarrow of St Ives Consols issued another special report on the current operation in which was stated that on the Malkin Lode the water was now forked to the 60-fathom level, the bottom of the shaft being at the 70-fathom level. Also the 25-fathom level was being cleared west on Bosiliack Lode and the 40-fathom level was being driven south on Bussa Lode and was within 10 fathoms of Bosiliack Lode which had previously yielded great profits in the shallow workings. The 40-fathom level was being cleared north of Bussa Lode which, he said, had formerly been productive, and on Tallow Lode the 40-fathom level was being driven west, a little to the west of Malkin Lode, and going into unexplored ground. Bussa Lode trends north-south and lies in the western part of the set. It is intersected by Bosiliack Lode at its southern end, apparently terminating the ore shoots as there are no stopes south of here. The central part of the lode is intersected by Malkin, After's, Black, Bolitho's, Ding Dong and Wheal Boys lodes, where the lode was most extensively developed, particularly from surface.[46] The most northerly intersection is with the shallow-dipping Green's Lode, beyond which there are no more stopes.

The old Ding Dong Engine Shaft was still being forked by flat rods from the western engine (the Greenburrow 40-inch), and in the eastern part of the mine the 30-inch at Tredinnick Shaft was put to work again, pumping Providence Shaft via an 80-fathom run of flat rods.

Providence Shaft had been sunk on Jilbert's Lode where little work had been done above the 60-fathom level, and where no tin had been discovered, but a good bunch of ore was reported at the intersection of Jilbert's and Rowe's Lodes, and there was also good tin ground west of the shaft which, he said, extended 4 fathoms below the level. The 70-fathom level had been driven 15 fathoms west of Providence Lode and from 8 to 10 fathoms west of the latter. Tin had been broken to the value of £12, but none was found elsewhere in the 70-fathom level. Two winzes had been sunk below this level, one east of the shaft and the other to the west, and tin had been discovered in each. In the western winze £150 worth of tin had been produced from the first four fathoms, but the deposit was short and was soon worked out. The lode had improved to the 80-fathom level and the winze, and the richest of the tin, he stated, inclined to the east of the workings.

The 80-fathom level was driven east of this winze through a rich lode and holed into the shaft. The eastern winze had shown signs of improvement from the 70-fathom level in length and was within three fathoms of holing into the shaft. He also observed that the tin came into the shaft five fathoms below the 70-fathom level, where it was estimated to be worth £20 per fathom, and it improved downwards to the bottom of the shaft which was seven feet below the 80-fathom level, *i.e.* 487 feet. Here a good lode had been found which was three feet wide and composed chiefly of tin and quartz and was estimated as being worth £140 per fathom. In the 80-fathom level west the lode was two feet wide, worth £35 per fathom and the lode in the 80-fathom level east of the eastern winze was 2½ feet wide and valued at £80 per fathom. The total number employed at this time was about 130, with 50 men on tutwork, 20 tributers, and about 60 on the surface.[47]

The winter of 1865-66 seems to have been even worse than that of 1836-37, resulting in a "coal famine" due to the bad weather.[48] The whole of the coal traffic between Wales and Penzance had been affected and vessels loaded at Neath since the middle of December had only started landing near the end of January. Ding Dong and all of the St Just mines bar three had nearly exhausted their coal stocks. It was only due to the fact that Messrs. Coulson in Penzance had kept unusually large stocks in their Penzance depot that mine agents were able to avoid partial suspensions of engines. Some colliers tried several times to leave Wales but were driven back. One vessel had arrived off the Longships Lighthouse on January 23rd, but, the wind having fallen off, the vessel had drifted backwards and forwards with the tide and did not arrive in Penzance until the 27th.

The financial quarter ending December 1865 showed a profit of £46 17s 11d although this left a small deficit against the mine. At the meeting it was decided that relinquished shares could be bought by other shareholders at £2 per share on the basis that the sellers had paid any and all outstanding calls. The number of shares transferred, 89½, is the same number as transferred in December 1864 and it is possible that there was a legal time limit to allow transfer. The sale of these shares raised £164 6s. During the first quarter of 1866 work was still concentrated in the eastern end of the mine. In Tredinnick Engine Shaft a skip road and plunger lift were being fixed and Providence Shaft was being sunk below the 80-fathom level. A new whim engine house was also being built, Ishmael's, by Elisha Marks and company. The engine appears to have been a new 25-inch from Sandys Vivian & Co. of Copperhouse and cost £300. Additional costs, such as masons' wages, timber, etc. brought the engine's costs to £405; despite this the mine only suffered a loss on three months of £94 19s 8d, and a balance against the mine of £190 10s 3d was carried forward. Unfortunately, by June the adverse balance was £868 13s 1d and a call of £1 per share was made. A total of £99 18s was owed on unpaid shares and the purser was authorised to act accordingly.

In April that year the mine paid Henry Richards £4 "towards loss of cow in shaft.[49] Richards was a local farmer and stone carrier, living at Church Downs, Madron.[50]

September 1866 saw a deficit of £385 12s 10d on the previous three months' working, to which the added balance of £190 10s 11d from the last account, ending March, resulted in a debit of £576 3s 9d. In the six months account, audited to the end of June, the cost of a new whim engine was charged, amounting to about £650.[51] Amongst this was another payment for Elisha Marks and his crew of masons:

<u>July 1866</u>
Elisha Marks and company sundry mason work in
bolt leading to Tredinnick Engine Shaft

Elisha Marks and company building engine & boiler
for 25-in whim engine 481 perchs @ 5/3, laying roof
161 1/3 square @ 9/-, putting in boiler house complete,
brickwork on top of stack, striking scaffolding, whitewashing,
levelling flywheel cage & cylinder loadings,
top of bob end   £144-15-5

The agent's report stated that in Greenburrow Engine Shaft the 40-, 60- and 70-fathom levels had been driven during the quarter, and there were reports of a promising lode in the 70-fathom level. Ding Dong Shaft had been cleared to the bottom (80 fathoms) and in the same shaft driving on several lodes had been started.

In the Providence section the stopes in the bottom of the 90-fathom level had been valued at £40 per fathom, and the 80-fathom level west was reported as containing rich stones of tin, valued at £15 per fathom. The report concluded on an optimistic note by remarking that the shareholders could now look up their holdings in the mine as a thoroughly safe and bona fide investment.

During August, September and October work was being carried out at Ding Dong Engine Shaft, which was being cut down (possibly where rock was loose as the shaft had been open for a very long time) and a skip road fitted. It is unclear which engine was winding from this shaft as both whims had horizontal drums and neither faced the shaft (a winding drum with a vertical axle could be used to wind from a large number of shafts), however Ishmael's seems the most likely after due consideration. Tredinnick Engine Shaft was being cleared below the 110-fathom level while the 100-fathom level was being driven west on Frederick's Lode. In the December account the balance against the mine of £10 0s 6d was carried forward and it was resolved that a working plan and sections of the mine be made. It is difficult to estimate the number of workers employed from the cost book. In February 1867 there were 39 persons employed at the stamps with 30 tutwork bargains and 15 tribute bargains recorded. The bargains themselves covered groups of men and only the actual taker's name was recorded.

Analysis of the shareholders during this period is interesting and shows the tight hold on the mine that the Bolithos and other local shareholders had. After relinquishments the mine was in 656 shares. Of these, 324 (49%) were held by the Bolitho company and a total of 485 (74%) were held by inhabitants of Penzance. Forty shares were held by other Cornish addresses and two in Devon, the rest being spread between London and Lancashire. At the meeting at held at Bolitho's offices at Chyandour in March 1867 it was stated that the mine had sold 45 tons of concentrate in three months; the highest price had been £54 per ton, and £202 profit realised. The prospects were looking exceedingly good and shares had recently changed hands for "some pounds".[52]

A year later, in September 1867, the accounts showed a credit balance of £356 19s 6d and a dividend of 10s per share was declared. During the three months working, 44 tons, 11 cwts. 3 qrs., 22 lb. of tin were sold at an average price of £54 11s 6d per ton. The agent's report was still encouraging, stating that at Providence Shaft the 70-fathom level south was worth £25 per fathom, a stope in the back of the 90-fathom level had been valued at £50 per fathom, and in the back of the 80-fathom level a stope was said to be worth £35 per fathom. On Jilbert's Lode the 70-fathom level was reported to be worth £40 per fathom and a winze, being sunk below the 60-fathom level, at £10 per fathom.[53]

In March 1868 John Truran's name disappeared from the cost book and it appears that he was replaced by William Williams, senior to Thomas Daniel.[54]

This is also the first reference to Thomas Daniel, who may have replaced Matthew; possibly they were relatives. The dry was being repaired in May and there is a reference to John Eustice removing "flywheel &c. at Wheal Reeth, 12 days, £3-6-0", suggesting that one of the whims or the stamps engine needed some spare parts. During July and August a tramroad was being built, presumably the one connecting Ishmael's whim to the stamps. In January 1868 a William Williams, not the agent, was given 8s from the doctor's club.[55] His name also comes up in April that year, though the reason for the entry is unclear. However at the bottom of the page is the following entry:

Coffin	2 10 0	
Parson, clerk &	10 0	W. Williams funeral expences
Girls' attendance	4 0	
Spirit to house/p bills	5 9	

In August, new stamps were erected; it is unclear if these were extra heads or replacements. The eastern section of the mine was all but worked out. At Tredinnick Shaft the workings had ultimately reached the depth of 135 fathoms (810 feet) but at greater depths the ground showed no signs of improvement, and by the mid 1860s the future of the mine depended on the workings to the west, and especially the western and of the Malkin Lode.[56] Between the latter and Ding Dong lay Wheal Ishmael (SW 441 349) which had formerly been a part of the Ding Dong sett. Shortly before the abandonment of its deeper levels, in or around 1844, a connecting passage had been driven between Wheal Ishmael and Ding Dong, and in 1864, owing to the discovery of a rich deposit of ore in an adjoining working, it was decided to unwater the old Ding Dong workings and also recommence working Wheal Ishmael. In the course of draining these old parts of the mines there was a most unusual occurrence. In response to the reduced level of operations the workforce had dropped and now stood at 120, comprising 100 men, 10 females and 10 boys.[57]

The task of de-watering commenced some four years later and in order to drain Wheal Ishmael it was found that due to the fact that Ishmael's workings were some feet below the Ding Dong section it was necessary to put in a siphon to convey the water to the pumping engine (presumably the Tredinnick 30-inch). On Friday August 7th 1868, two workmen, Ralph Daniel and James

Harry, waded through an accumulation of slime and water in the level in order to carry out the installation. Suddenly there was a violent explosion and both men were knocked off their feet and badly scalded. A few days later the managing agent, Captain William Williams, "tested the air" with a candle attached to the end of a long staff. An even greater explosion ensued but this time no one was injured. After a short interval Captain Thomas Daniel entered carrying a naked candle and this time there was a terrific explosion which very nearly cost him his life. After that no one was allowed access until Davy safety lamps had been procured.

When this had been done, Samuel Higgs, the secretary to the Royal Geological Society of Cornwall (and mine shareholder), accompanied Captain Williams and one of the pitmen into the level. The men observed that the flame in their lamps became elongated and also displayed a bluish halo, indicating the presence of methane gas, better known in collieries as 'fire-damp'. This had been caused by old and rotting timbers which, until recently, had been all but submerged. According to Higgs it was evident that the backs had previously been worked, and subsequently they had either been filled with rubbish or had run together, and from the 'peculiar freshness' of the granite at the place where the gas had been encountered, it was clear that although the mine had been full of water for 10 fathoms above, none had lodged here and that over the years the gas had accumulated in this level. There had only been one other recorded case of fire damp in a Cornish mine in 1791, but the location is unknown. However seventeen men were reportedly killed in an explosion

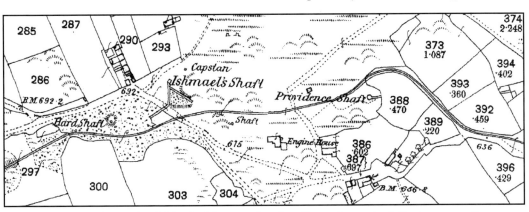

Detail of the 1st series 25-inch OS map showing the main part of the tramway from the dressing floors to the west to Ishmael's whim and, ulimately, Tredinnick Shaft to the east.

so violent that it hurled the mine's head frame for some considerable distance before it landed on a cottage, entirely destroying it and killing the unfortunate inhabitant.[58]

Yet another accident happened later that month.[59] On August 24th the engineman, John Dunn, of Madron, was talking to Hannibal Eddy, a boy employee from Towednack. For some unknown reason Eddy was lying across the rod that connected the flywheel of the engine to the tozing machines (kieves), resting on both hands. Suddenly the engine must have turned suddenly and the turning rod caught his loose frock, flinging him round with such force that it tore off one of his arms near the shoulder, following which the force of the rod threw him away. The engine was stopped immediately, although too late, and two doctors were summoned. The remains of his arm were amputated, but Eddy died three hours later.

The second half of 1868 was another high point for the mine's profits. In June a modest profit of £9 0s 7d was recorded, although there was a debit balance of £283 10s against the mine.[60] In September the three months profit was £316 8s 3d and the adverse balance was £32 18s 3d. In December the balance in favour of the mine had leapt to £1,115 10s 9d; a dividend of £1 10s per share was authorised (equal to £984) leaving a balance of £131 10s 9d to be carried forward. As a token of appreciation, purser Richard Wellington was presented with a gift of twenty guineas, Captain Joseph Tregonning twelve guineas and Captain Thomas Daniel three guineas in consideration

List of engine men and their wages in November 1869.

144

of their extra services for some time past and up to the present time. Daniel's salary was also to be increased by one guinea per month, from £6 6s to £7 7s, from January. It was stated by the *Cornish Telegraph* reported that a valuable discovery had been made in the 80-fathom level in the Providence section, which was said to be worth £30 per fathom.[61] Also the 60- and 70-fathom levels were opening up good tin ground and at surface, where the stamps and dressing floors were being enlarged, there lay about 20 tons of stock tin.

The profits continued into 1870, with a positive balance of £1,204 8s 5d in March, £1,136 17s 1d in June and £764 12s 2d in December.[62] Tin sales had been between 45 and 49 tons, fetching prices of around £74 per ton. To use up these profits dividends were given of £1 10s in March and June and £1 in September, totalling £2,624.

On Saturday May 1st there was yet another accident.[63] William Stone, of Bosworthen, Madron, along with two companions, William Rowe and Richard Trembath, had been at work in the 70-fathom level and had encountered some loose rock which seemed poised to fall at any moment. On the previous day Rowe and Trembath warned Stone that the ground should be taken down before any further work was carried out. Stone agreed with this but said that it might be left until Monday when the Captains would see to it, but shortly afterwards he removed some 10 to 12 barrows of stuff from the back of the level, and this further weakened the ground. The three men were at their place of work the next day and Stone, on striking the piece of ground with a hammer, remarked that it sounded "drummy" and added that it would have to be taken down. Suddenly about seven or eight tons of rock fell on him; he was extricated with great difficulty and taken to his home where, due to severe internal injuries, he died two days later.

The following month the agents reported that the mine was looking well and that work on the stamps and dressing floors was under way. They further disclosed that in the course of laying open the mine at different points and particularly the Providence section, several new lodes had been discovered and, as far as current exploration went, were found to be productive. In the same report it was stated that 115 men were employed on tutwork and 8 on tribute.[64]

In January 1870, according to the agent's report, there were then five engines at work on the mine, and the workforce had been increased.[65] The *Williams' Mining Directory* for that year states that the total number employed was 222 but according to the *Mining Journal* of June 4th, 194 were employed, including 68 tutworkers and 44 tributers. On Saturday 25th May 1872 the Ding Dong miners struck over a change in the hours that were to be worked.[66] It is unclear when the change took place but the management seems to have acceded very quickly and the old hours (work to finish at 2pm on Saturdays and mid-day on pay-days) were restored. The 'owners' account men', generally the lowest paid workers, were obliged to work until 3pm on Saturdays.

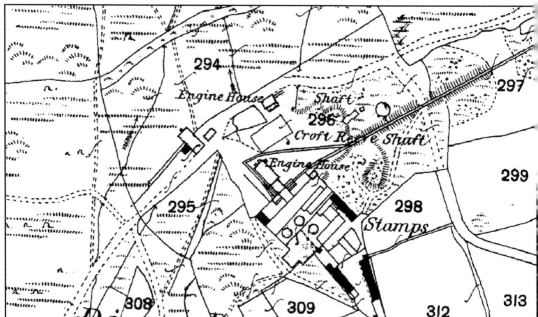

Ding Dong Mine, area of the dressing floors and the older of the two whim engines. 1st Series 25-inch OS map.

The early 1870s witnessed another rise in tin prices. In 1866 black tin had fallen to £48 per ton but shortly afterwards it slowly began to climb, and by 1870 it was up to £75 per ton and rising. In 1872 it had reached £87 per ton but by the next year the price began to fall once again. The cause of the slump was that vast deposits of tin had been discovered in Queensland, both in lode form and in widespread alluvial deposits. Sales of imported tin were by no means a new occurrence, and since about 1850 small quantities had been sold either in London or Liverpool. However, these recent discoveries greatly surpassed the quantities formerly imported and furthermore the ore was much easier to extract than in Cornwall. In most instances all that was required was a shovel and a pan for the washing of the ore, and in many places even these articles could be dispensed with as it was possible to pick up lumps of almost pure cassiterite (tin oxide) which lay exposed in the dry river beds. Australian overproduction coupled with mass importation resulted in a rapid decline in the price of Cornish tin which, in 1873, fell from £87 to £78 per ton.[67]

Optimistic reports continued to circulate, but in reality the mine was nearing exhaustion and had been showing increasing signs of such over the previous ten years or so. That the eastern section was already worked out has been established, but where hope now lay, towards the west, only constant expansion at shallower levels prevailed. The principal trouble was the nature of the lodes themselves as, although numerous, none amounted to the dimensions of large bodies of ore such as the great Carbona Lode of St Ives Consols. Also there were the financial difficulties.

For the quarter to December 1870, the costs, wages etc amounted to £1,641 16s 4d, and the merchants bills, coals, dues and rents a further £447 15s 1d, giving a total of £2,089 12s 4d.[68] Tin produced was 25 tons 13 cwt, selling for an average price £74 per ton. There was a deficit on the quarter of £62 6s 10d but still a balance in favour of the mine of £99 17s 8d. Tredinnick Shaft was sinking at £15 per fathom and was looking kindly for tin. The winze below the 125-fathom level was worth £8 per fathom and the stopes in the back were worth £5. The 125-fathom level was the deepest part of the operations. The workforce of 227 included 141 men on tutwork.

During 1871 there was a tailing off of profits, with losses reported in June and September, and at the meeting of 5 December 1871 (for the September account) it was reported that the balance of £460 7s 2d against the mine would be carried forward "with distinct understanding that at the end of the next quarter unless the prospects of the mine should considerably improve a call be made to pay off the balance". The areas of operations at this time had not changed for over two years, viz. Tredinnick Engine Shaft, Providence Shaft and Croft Reeve Shaft. Tredinnick Engine Shaft was the busiest section with operations on the 120-fathom level (three pares), 110-fathom level (two), 135-fathom level (two) and the 125-fathom level (four). In all there were

147

39 tutwork bargains in the mine. Despite the tone of the September account meeting, the adverse balance for the following quarter was £982 4s 8d. The mine continued with a call of 30s per share although there were now only 67 shareholders; a 5% discount for prompt payment was offered.

Of the all too frequent number of accidents, both underground and at surface, the most tragic were surely those involving children. On July 8th 1873 two bal maidens, Alice Ann Stevens and Eliza Jane Hall, both employed at the stamps, met in the stamps boiler house during their dinner break and from there went on to the nearby whim house.[69] Shortly afterwards Stevens went to a nearby stream (probably one of the leats supplying water for the dressing floors and/ or engine boilers) to wash her hands while Hall climbed on to the crown wheel of the whim, which was stationary at the time. Stevens admonished the foolish girl saying, "Eliza, don't you know better than to go up there?" Hall made no reply but climbed down from the wheel. Just at that moment the signal bell rang, indicating that the engine was about to start, and Hall, ignoring a second warning from Stevens, climbed back onto the wheel which was now in motion, exclaiming, "I will go round". The wheel had the motion of a roundabout, but proved to be a very dangerous one to ride, for in an instant the girl's clothes were caught in it and she was dragged to the ground.

On hearing Stevens' scream, James Berryman, the whim driver, stopped the engine. Hall was found lying partly on the ground and partly on the cog of the wheel, and on freeing her it was discovered that her right leg had passed through the wheel and was crushed and broken. Her left foot, having been caught in the cogs, was extensively fractured and blood was also dripping onto the ground. Despite prompt medical attention by Dr Montgomery the poor girl died seven hours later. At the inquest, Berryman stated that the crown wheel had been in use at the mine for over twenty years and this was the first accident that had happened with it. "No boy or girl had any business on or near the wheel", he added. Eliza's risk at trying to ride on the wheel was presumably down to her not having worked at the mine for very long. Had she more experience it seems unlikely that she would have attempted climbing anywhere on the engine.

The mine's doctor's club book[70] gives the following accounts:

Eliza Hall's funeral expences	2-14-0
Mrs Grenfell, per bill for coffin do.	2-7-0
Cabe (cab) Hire Eliza Hall's inquest	10-0
Hire of Rooms for do.	2-6
Dr Montgomery's Fee for attending Eliza Hall	1-1-0

Eliza was buried in an unmarked grave at Gulval Church. Following initial enquiries from Lynne Mayers, the enthusiastic researcher of bal maidens, the grave was eventually discovered. Money for a headstone was raised by Madron Old Cornwall Society and on 12th July 2013 a short commemorative service was held to dedicate the new headstone, which had been erected *gratis* by the undertaker, Walker's of Penzance. Interestingly she is buried next to

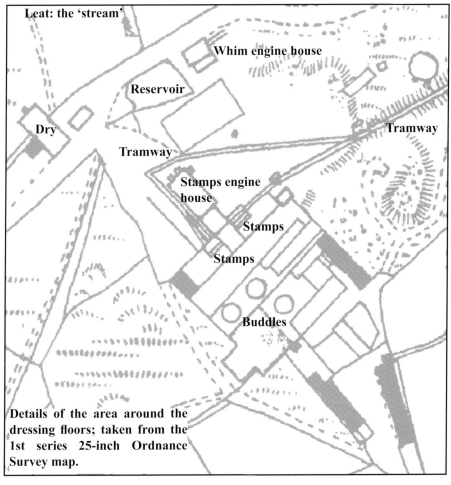

Details of the area around the dressing floors; taken from the 1st series 25-inch Ordnance Survey map.

three different Doctor Montgomery's, all of the same family.

It should be noted that this accident did not take place at Ishmeal's whim, the only currerntly extant whim engine house, but at the old whim engine house, formerly situated a few yards to the north-east of the stamps engine (see map overleaf).

August 1873 saw the appearance of two new agents, Thomas P. Rowe and Richard Bennetts, the latter possibly working part-time as he was paid less than half the former's salary.[71] The September account showed that work was still concentrated at the eastern end of the sett, at Ishmael's Shaft (mostly on Robin's Lode at the 50, 60 and 70-fathom levels), Tredinnick Engine Shaft (on a slide lode) and Providence Shaft (sinking below, and driving at, the 100-fathom level). Richard Bennetts was absent from the cost book for that month and did not return.

In December 1873 it was disclosed that the mine was spending nearly £10,000 in labour costs, over £4,000 in merchant's bills etc., and above £2,000 on coal. The last account showed that 60 tons, 2 cwt., 2 qrs. of tin had been sold at an average price of £72 19s per ton, giving a total of £4,386 3s to meet the expenses of the previous sixteen weeks working, which amounted to £4,297 13s. The cost book showed the following:

Tutworkers' wages	£1,606
Materials	£673
549 tons, 16 cwts. of coal at 18s 9d per ton	£516
Surface men's wages	£358
Stamps wages	£319
Carriage & haulage	£216
Tribute	£213
Engine-men and pitmen	£170
Purser, agency, clerk etc	£126
Doctor & Club	£30
Total	£4,227

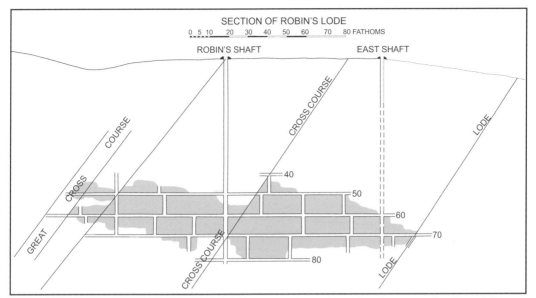

Section of Robin's Lode showing the concentration of stoping between the 40 and 80 fathom levels. Mineralisation on the lode appears to have been cut off by a crosscourse on one side and a lode on the other. Redrawn from Cornwall Record Office document MRO 1162-11.

and the remaining £70 13s in miscellaneous items.

The overall picture for 1874 was a gloomy one as the price of tin had fallen drastically, to £56 per ton. In December the accounts showed that 62 tons of ore had been sold for £3,497 (£56 8s per ton), and there now stood a balance of £3,460 against the mine, which was then employing 273 persons.[72]

In July 1875 Thomas Cock, a sawyer at the mine, met with a serious accident.[73] Having been called to assist in replacing a tram wagon which had left the rails, the bar which he was using to lift the wagon slipped, and he fell back off the tramway, a height of twelve feet, onto rocks below. Cock received several severe cuts on the head and such an injury to his back that Dr Davy was called to attend to the injuries. The month saw a loss on sixteen weeks working of £563. Sixty-three tons of tin ore had been sold for £3,259, whilst the total expenses amounted to £3,774. The loss of £563 included a debit balance of £48 from the previous account. The total number employed was 265 which included 136 men and boys on tutwork and 10 men on tribute.[74] In October a call of £1 per share was made to meet an adverse balance of £925.[75]

151

The agent's report for December 1875 indicated that the most valuable points in the mine were at the 70-fathom level, east of the cross-course on Robin's Lode which was being driven at £10 per fathom, and was valued at £30 per fathom.[76] Robin's Lode lies north of the central part of the sett and trends WNW-ESE, with the western end of the lode veering to the WSW. It is intersected at its western end by the Great Crosscourse, which appears to terminate the run of tin, while an intersection with an un-named lode at the eastern end terminates the ore shoot at that end. The lode was not developed above the 40-fathom level.[77] Two stopes in the back of the same level were being driven at £2 17s 6d per fathom and were said to be worth £30 per fathom.

Three stopes in the same level west were being driven at £3 18s per fathom, and were valued at £20. On the same lode, in the back of the 60-fathom level, driving had been set at £3 7s 6d per fathom and the pitch was valued at £14 per fathom. The northern part of the level was being driven at £5 10s per fathom and the value of the lode was set at £25. Robin's Shaft was then being sunk below the 20-fathom level by 9 men at £19 per fathom, where the lode, 18 inches wide, was reported as very promising.

The price of tin in 1875 was £53 per ton and this dropped even further in the following year, to £44. In February a call of £1 per share was made to try to counter the adverse balance.[78] In July there was a report of what was alleged to be a valuable discovery at a depth of about 80 fathoms, and which was first valued at £100 per fathom and later at £150 but time was rapidly running out for the mine.[79]

The first rumours of closure were aired by the *Cornish Telegraph* in February 1877.[80] By this time the price of tin had fallen to £41 per ton and with closure of many notable mines in the county, it was now Ding Dong's turn to bow to the inevitable. In May the following notice appeared in the *Mining Journal*:[81]

> There is but one month left to the neighbourhood, this very old, and at times, very productive mine, and to hope against hope that it may not be stopped, but it is feared that Queensland and Tasmania will cause the suspension – it may be for a short, and it may be for an extended period - of this enterprise. The Bolitho family have held a considerable share of it for 140 years, and for the last two years have owned nearly

half the mine, but the old associations, invested capital, the well doing of a locality, all must yield to the competitive and low price of South Australian tin. At a meeting of Ding Dong adventurers held on Monday, a loss was shown, on 16 weeks work, of £800, although rigid economy has been practised on the mine for many years (every liability that can possibly be ascertained has been discharged up to the day of the meeting) and thus the shareholders made a final call of £2 per share; and unless some friendly 'knocker' or other subterranean fairy shows Ding Dong miners a good course of ore within the next 20 days, Ding Dong's knell will be rung out from the Dolmen of Zennor to Lanyon Quoit.

The mine continued to operate although it must have been clear that its time was over. At the April account there was a loss on twenty weeks working of £826, giving a total adverse balance of £1,322 11s 3d.[82] A call of £2 per share was made for the remaining 37 shareholders for June 2nd and the purser was instructed to immediately enforce payment of all unpaid calls (totalling £48 11s 5d). The agents were instructed to continue to drive the 80-fathom level east and the 70-fathom level north on Robin's Lode and suspend all other tutwork.

Less than three months later Ding Dong ceased working, on the 11th of July, and the mine was offered for sale as a going concern. Two bids for the mine, one of £1,050 and the other at £1,200, were made by Messrs. Bolitho who proposed to work it for at least six months as a new company in 1,000 shares.[83] The account for the sixteen weeks ending July gave the purchase money as £1,185 and a positive balance of £162 13s 3d although there had been a loss on the period of £873 6s 6d. In November the workforce was reduced to 64, including six enginemen, three agents, seven at surface and twenty-five at the stamps. The mine appears to have limped on for some months in increasingly antagonistic economic times, with continued losses, but at the end of January 1878 the mine was "knacked and all hands paid off".[84] It had employed over 500 persons in better times but the number had "dangerously dwindled" to 150 in recent times owing to the decline of the price of tin caused by imports from Australia and elsewhere. The present employees had not been working full time, the mine having had "but a bare existence" for some months.

Mining Journal **advertisement for the sale of the mine's machinery and materials from March 1878.**

A meeting regarding the alleged distress in west Cornwall, caused by mine closures, was held in March 1878.[85] At the meeting, Thomas S. Bolitho said he hoped the closure of Ding Dong was only temporary as a large number of people had been thrown out of work. "But who were they? There was not a good man amongst them, for the best, seeing bad times approaching, had struggled to get away. One man lately came to see him saying he had eight children at home, and six used to help him at Ding Dong. And that was the sort of inferior labourers who were left behind." Bolitho was a former Poor Board Guardian and one wonders if his views were representative.

One person who had seen the light was James Russell Curnow, son of James Curnow of Ding Dong and nephew of John N. Russell of Penzance.[86] James had left the mine because of poor earnings and gone to California where he attended the University of the Pacific. After four years of study he graduated in medicine, having supported himself by working during the vacations. In March 1878 the materials at Ding Dong New Adventure, as the mine was re-named, were put up for auction.[87] Little else is recorded by the cost books beyond tidying the mine, filling and fencing shafts. In November Thomas Daniel, the single agent, was paid six guineas while John Williams was paid various sums for working at the shafts:

for filling   Willey's (Withey's?) Shaft   £1 15s

154

for fencing Wheal Boys Shaft	£2 5s
Highburrow Shaft	£1 17s 6d
Tallow Shaft	£1 0s
Greenpease Shaft	14s 4d

The fencing and filling work finished by 1 February 1879 and the mine was finally abandoned; the company went into receivership on June 28th, 1880, following payment of a final dividend in Fenruary.[88] The final dividend paid 18th February 1880 was:

Name	No. shares	Amount
Bolitho	339	£186 19s
William Seward	23	£12 13s
Miss W. Forster	20	£11 0s
Owen Jones	20	£11 0s
J. Coulson & Co.	16	£8 16s
Richard Wellington	14	£7 14s
John Whitwell	11	£6 1s
N. Holman & Sons	10	£5 10s

plus 23 others (total 526 shares), 11s/share dividend

Year	Tonnage	Value
1855	130.20	£8,849.60
(146.00 £9,809.00 Journal Stat Soc London)		
1856	212.30	£17,214.80
1857	115.80	£9,420.30
1858	63.20	£4,312.00
1859	60.00	£4,902.30
1860	80.70	£6,722.70
1861	93.00	£6,553.00
1862	65.80	£4,357.10
1863	58.40	£4,042.30
1864	62.30	£3,523.40

1865	49.60	£2,691.30
1866	161.30	£8,219.50
1867	170.20	£9,371.00
1868	190.30	£11,636.10
1869	182.40	£13,413.10
1870	126.30	£9,818.00
1871	100.20	£8,236.70
1872	121.40	£10,500.20
1873	199.10	£14,469.80
1844	268.20	£15,206.60
1875	201.10	£10,276.10
1876	159.50	£7,002.10
1877	77.30	£2,781.00
1878	9.90	£350.10
Total	**2,958.50**	**£154,265.10**

Mineral production 1855-1878[89]

Chapter 9 references

1. Cornwall Record Office document RG 101: Ding Dong Mine cost book
2. Another Berryman, William, had been the Dispensing Apothecary at the Penzance Public Dispensary and Humane Society (the fore-runner of the West Cornwall Infirmary and Dispensary, later the West Cornwall Hospital) in 1824. The relationship of these Berrymans to each other is not known however William would have been old enough to have been their father.
3. *Cornish Telegraph* 20.6.1851
4. Cornwall Record Office document RG100: Ding Dong Mine cost book
5. *Cornish Telegraph* 30.5.1851
6. *Mining Journal* 20.3.1852
7. Cornwall Record Office document RG94: Ding Dong Mine cost book
8. Cornwall Record Office document RG101: Ding Dong Mine cost book
9. *Cornish Telegraph* 30 March 1853
10. Cornwall Record Office document RG94: Ding Dong Mine cost book
11. Barton, D. B., 1967. *A History of Tin Mining and Smelting in Cornwall*. Bradford Barton Ltd, Truro, pp99 and 110

12. *Mining Journal* 12.12.1856

13. *Mining Journal* 15.3.1856

14. *Mining Journal* 14.3.1857 and Brown, K. and Acton, B., 2001. *Exploring Cornish Mines*, Vol. 2. Landfall Publications, p169

15. *Mining Journal* 6.6.1857

16. *Mining Journal* 5.9.1857

17. *Mining Journal* 29.8.1857

18. *Mining Journal* 7.11.1857

19. *Mining Journal* 5.12.1857

20. Cornwall Record Office document MRO 1162-15: Ding Dong Mine plan

21. Cornwall Record Office document RG94: Ding Dong Mine cost book

22. *Mining Journal* 19.12.1857

23. *Mining Journal* 6.2.1858

24. *Mining Journal* 6.3.1858

25. *West Briton* 23.11.1857

26. Cornwall Record Office document RG95: Ding Dong Mine cost book

27. *Mining Journal* 5.11.1859

28. *Mining Journal* 17.12.1859

29. *Cornish Telegraph* 20.3.1861

30. *Cornish Telegraph* 9.10.1861

31. Noall C., 1989. *Cornish Mine Disasters*, Dyllansow Truran, p178

32. *Cornish Telegraph* 9.12.1863

33. Cornwall Record Office document RG96: Ding Dong cost book

34. Spargo, T., 1864. *The Mines of Cornwall and Devon*, Emily Faithfull, London, p17

35. *Cornish Telegraph* 25.5.1864

36. Spargo, T., 1864. *Statistics and Observations on the Mines of Cornwall.* Darlington & Son, London, p17.

37. *Cornish Telegraph* 15.1.1865

38. Spargo, T., 1865. *The Mines of Cornwall*, Emily Faithfull, London, p29

39. *Mining Journal* (extract per Justin Brooke)

40. *Mining Journal* 18 November 1865

41. Barton, D. B., 1967 *op. cit.* p110

42. *Mining Journal* 11.11.1865

43. *Mining Journal* 25.11.1865

44. *Cornish Telegraph* 22.11.1865

45. *Cornish Telegraph* 6.12.1865

46. Cornwall Record Office document MRO 1162-7: Ding Dong Mine plan

47. *Mining Journal* 16.12.1865

48. *Cornish Telegraph* 31.1.1866

49. *Cornish Telegraph* 29.9.1866

50. Cornwall Record Office document RG/104: Ding Dong Mine doctor's club book

51. 1861 census

52. *Cornish Telegraph* 13.3.1867

53. *Mining Journal* 21.9.1867

54. Cornwall Record Office documents RG97 and RG98: Ding Dong Mine cost books (the two books overlap)

55. Cornwall Record Office document RG/104: Ding Dong Mine doctor's club book

56. *Cornish Telegraph* 11.8.1868 and Transactions of the Royal Geological Society of Cornwall vol. 9 p35

57. Spargo, T., 1868. *The Mines of Cornwall and Devon*, Emily Faithfull, London, p197

58. *Cornish Telegraph* 11.8.1868 and Transactions of the Royal Geological Society of Cornwall vol. 9 p35

59. Noall, C., 1989, *op. cit.*, p178

60. Cornwall Record Office document RG98: Ding Dong Mine cost book

61. *Cornish Telegraph* 30.12.1868

62. Cornwall Record Office document RG98: Ding Dong Mine cost book

63. *Cornish Telegraph* 12.5.1869

64. *Cornish Telegraph* 16.6.1869

65. *Cornish Telegraph* 5.1.1870

66. *Royal Cornwall Gazette* 8.6.1872

67. Barton, D. B., 1967, *op. cit.*

68. *Cornish Telegraph* 15.3.1871

69. Noall, C., 1989, *op. cit.*, pp174-5

70. Cornwall Record Office document RG98: Ding Dong Mine cost book

71. Cornwall Record Office document RG 104 Ding Dong doctor's club book

72. *Mining Journal* 5.12.1874

73. *Cornish Telegraph* 28.7.1875

74. *Cornish Telegraph* 7.7.1875

75. *Cornish Telegraph* 20.12.1875

76. *Cornish Telegraph* 24.12.1875

77. Cornwall Record Office document MRO 1162-11: Ding Dong Mine plan

78. *Cornish Telegraph* 9 February 1876

79. *Cornish Telegraph* 1.8.1876

80. *Cornish Telegraph* 6.2.1877

81. *Cornish Telegraph* 22.5.1877

82. Cornwall Record Office document RG100: Ding Dong Mine cost book

83. *Mining World* 14.7.1877

84. *Cornish Telegraph* 29.1.1878

85. *Cornish Telegraph* 5.3.1878

86. *Cornish Telegraph* 4.2.1880

87. *Cornish Telegraph* 12.3.1878

88. Cornwall Record Office document RG100: Ding Dong Mine cost book

89. Burt, R., Waite, P. and Burnley, R., 1987. *The Cornish Mines*, University of Exeter, p.161

Chapter 10

Life After Death

In the year that saw the abandonment of Ding Dong the price of tin began to rise again. In 1878 the average price was £35 per ton, the next year it had crept up to £40, and was up another £9 in 1880. Many mines throughout the county were restarted although in the vicinity of Ding Dong there were no signs of renewed activity apart from an unsuccessful attempt to unwater Carn Galver Mine, which lay one and a quarter miles north-north-west.[1] The latter ceased operations in or around 1882, an event soon followed by a decline in Cornish tin mining that was to have a greater impact than anything previously experienced and from 1886 to 1898 there was virtually no respite.

By 1903 the price of tin had risen to £130 per ton, but the Cornish mining industry had not recovered from the depression of the 1890s. However, the price was sufficient for attention to be focussed on old burrows and heaps of tailings and by 1906 old mines had reopened and a large number of new companies had been formed.[2] This boom coincided with the introduction of the more economical means of pumping by electrical power and the first mine in the vicinity of Ding Dong to be re-worked was Trewey Downs Mine, which lay one and a half miles north-east. The latter mine was worked intermittently during the last century with little or no success, as was the case with the attempt which ended in 1909. Two years later the dumps at Ding Dong were explored by one John Osborne, a Cornish mining engineer, who was of the opinion that they might be worth exploiting. Accordingly, he took some ore samples to John Penberthy, the proprietor of the Carvossa tin stamping and dressing mills at Ludgvan and, after assaying a number of samples, both men concluded that there remained sufficient quantities of cassiterite in the waste heaps to be worth treating them. This was due to the less efficient methods of extraction employed in the previous century, and Penberthy decided that it would prove a lucrative speculation to work the dumps if the price of metallic tin ranged from £180 to £200 per ton.[3]

In 1912 a company was formed under the name of the Ding Dong Mining Syndicate, more familiarly known as Ding Dong Dumps. The company was formed after a trial period, in September, with a capital of £1,000 in £1 shares, and the principal shareholders were mostly Cornishmen who had returned from the gold mines of the Rand.

John Osborne, a native of Zennor, was a descendant of a landowning family of that parish and had been a mining engineer in the Transvaal. Penberthy came from a family of Lelant tin dressers and had also spent a number of years in the Transvaal. The two men became acquainted on board ship whilst on the long voyage back to Cornwall. Another to join this venture was one William Richards, a tin dresser who was nicknamed 'Yank Richards', owing to the American accent which he had acquired during his long stay in the United States.

Early in 1912 sufficient capital had been raised to enable them to erect some buildings on the slope of a hill by the side of Chyandour Stream (SW 441 342), near the hamlet at Carfury. A forty-year lease was obtained and ten heads of Cornish stamps, powered by a steam engine, were erected by Messrs. Holman of St Just, and were first put to work in July of the same year.[4] These had been ordered from the foundry in November the previous year for about £760 and appear to have been supplemented with another two heads early in 1912.[5]

The battery had a falling weight of 850-900 lbs. per head; other equipment included buddles and a round frame. Work soon began in earnest. The ore was transported from the dumps in hired horse-drawn carts working on a contract basis. In all, five carts were employed, three of which were owned by Thomas Noy of Boskednan and worked by his sons, one by William Hocken of Boskednan, and one by John Nicholls of Tredinnick.[6] The dumps by Ding Dong Shaft were the ones initially worked and proved to be of good quality. Also the ore from all the various dumps was soft and easily crushed – the resulting tin being of fine quality and so free milling that it did not require calcining. Some iron contained in the ore was easily removed by leaching out with sulphuric acid, but no arsenic or copper was present.

The running costs of the syndicate were fairly high, and the accounts from the 15th of January to December 31st 1912 showed the wages for the workers at the dumps, breaking and loading ore, and at the stamps, crushing and dressing, amounted to £669 2s 5d, £149 12s 9d for coal, and £150 15s 2d in carriage costs. It was further pointed out that although they had been paying an expenditure over a period of twelve months, they had only been receiving money since June 24th, and since that date they had sold 8 tons, 14 cwt., 3 qrs. and 11 lbs. of tin for £1,163 19s 4d, resulting in a profit of £143 16s 2d.[7]

The Syndicate was incorporated as a limited company in January 1913 with a capital of £1,050, and on Friday 10th, the first annual general meeting was held at the Western Hotel, Penzance. The reconstituted company was formed with the object of "carrying on the business of working and developing the Ding Dong Mine sett, and refining and preparing for market any ores found therein. It thus had the right to work the mine itself in addition to any china clay deposit which might be found on the property. George Godolphin, the Duke of Leeds, was involved with the mine at this time, suggesting that the Godolphin family may have held an interest in the sett for over 100 years.[8]

The board of directors consisted of five men: John Osborne, of 84 Main Street, Heamoor, John Penberthy, of Rospeath Villa, Ludgvan, William Richards, of 3 Lannoweth Terrace, Penzance, Arthur Pearse Jenkin, of Trewirgie, Redruth, and Horton Bolitho, of Penmere, Falmouth, the latter being a well-known figure in mining circles who was subsequently appointed as chairman of the company. The company's solicitor was Albert Edward Radcliffe, of Helston, and Edmund John Penberthy, the father of John Penberthy, was the company secretary. W. Matthews was the auditor.

Since the commencement of operations, dividends of 1s per share had been paid in November and December 1912,[9] but at the meeting of January 10th, 1913, Mr Matthews warned the company not to be in a hurry to make dividends too quickly, but instead build up a reserve fund as they should not expect tin to remain at its present price. One shareholder, John Gilbert, said that tin would go very much higher and everyone expected that it would reach £250 per ton. "The world supply is still below the demand", he remarked, "and as long as this is the case, the price will continue to rise". On asking the secretary what the profit was for the previous month, he was informed that it was £67 8s 5d – "A very fair profit on £1,000 capital" added Horton Bolitho. Mr Radcliffe then explained the legal position. He stated that there were several mineral lords interested and it had been rather difficult to get all their signatures on the lease. The two principal lords had signed, the lease was in the hands of the third for signature, and by the following week it would be fully signed.

They had the nominal rental of £20 per year, dues amounting to 1-20th, and a lease for 40 years. He further remarked upon the matter of capital. The sum had originally been decided upon when the company was started, "but", he warned, "if you want to increase that sum after registration, it will be a costly business". He therefore advised them to immediately increase their capital to £2,000 and therefore provide for contingencies.

In January 1913 a further four heads of stamps were added to the battery, making a total of sixteen in all, capable of handling 600 loads of stuff of about twenty-five hundredweights each per month.[10] It had been hoped that another eight head of stamps would be started in the ensuing summer months but unfortunately a prolonged drought caused Chyandour Stream to fall, and consequently the extra stamps were not brought in until November. The cost of the extra heads was £70. Power for the stamps was supplied by a steam engine which was fed from an upright boiler and the engine proved to be very economical to run.

The increased battery also meant a small increase in labour and one extra man and two boys had to be hired to run the now enlarged stamps. In addition two extra men were taken on to work at the dumps where the total workforce at the latter now amounted to eight men. In order to supplement the water supply, which was conveyed to the stamps via a series of wooden launders, an adit of Ding Dong Mine was opened up to the north-west of the site during the middle of 1913 and additional boiler water was obtained from this source.

During one evening shift in the same year, the boiler exploded, fortunately without fatal consequences, but the engine man was scalded. The boiler was quickly repaired by Messrs. Holman, who sent their own mechanics to the site.[11]

John Penberthy reported that in the previous September they had crushed 346 tons, 10 cwt. at a value of 9¼ lbs. of tin to the ton, in October at 8½ lbs., November 398 tons at 10 lbs. per ton, and 33 tons at 10½ lbs. per ton in December. Six parcels had been sent to the ticketing, the lowest price received being £120 and the highest at £135 2s 5d. He thought at one time that if he kept the leavings and sent it as a separate parcel, he might get a better value for the other, but instead of getting a higher price, quite the reverse occurred and that was the first and last time that that course was taken.[12] In April the company declared its third dividend of 1s per share.[13] Also deposits of china clay had been discovered and in June 1914 these were reported as amounting to millions of tons. The overburden was said to be only about six feet deep while the clay was known to be 70 fathoms in depth and was declared to be or the best quality.[14]

During the year 1913 a total of 5,363 tons of stuff had been crushed, yielding an average of 8.5 lbs. of black tin concentrate per ton. Much of this had come from burrows at Providence Shaft, and altogether 20 tons, 11 cwt., 27 lbs. of tin ore was sold at the price of £111 8s 8d per ton, realising a total of £2,291 7s 10d. Tin leavings produced a total of £28 7s and sales of sand amounted to £3 5s. The net profit for the year was £180 6s and the dividend for the year was seven per cent.[15] These figures, it would seem, indicated a bright future for the company but such was not the case. In 1913 the price of tin had dropped, and by January 1914 it stood at only £92 13s 6d per ton. Also, the market was affected by imported tin from Malaya and the East Indies as well as by strikes and other forms of industrial unrest at home.

At the beginning of 1914 the company's capital stood at £1,500 but extra calls had been made to pay for the new stamp heads and slimes plant. Then, in August, came the outbreak of war which was to drastically affect the industry throughout the county as men rushed to join the armed forces. The price of tin continued to fall and for the first time the company failed to make a profit. About 20 tons of black tin concentrate had been produced, an amount comparable with that of the previous year, but this had only realised £85 12s 6d a ton at the ticketing and the overall result for the year was a loss of £70

19s 4s. The only gap in the clouds was the china clay deposits, upon which several pits had been sunk on the moor, north of the mine.

Tin production dropped and by the early months of 1915 all operations at the plant were suspended. During the period from September 1912 to March 1915 a total of 13,649 tons of picked ore had been treated at the plant, yielding over 51 tons of black tin concentrate. In November 1915 the company mortgaged all its machinery, property and other assets for £200 in order to keep the company in being and for the maintenance of the machinery and equipment in readiness for a possible resumption of operations. In 1916 John Penberthy tried to revive interest in the company, declaring that if £600 could be raised for the purchase of Wilfley tables and Frue vanners to replace the buddles and frames of the previous working, a great saving would be made. He also maintained that if further capital could be raised, it would pay to work the china clay deposits as the Cornwall Electric Company's power lines crossed the property, and which could be tapped to work the clay plant. However nothing came of this and no further work was undertaken until after the war.

In 1918 Albert Fredrick Calvert, a distinguished Australian and descendant of a famous mining family, endeavoured to boost the Cornish mining industry and started by reopening a group of mines around Gwinear. In August 1919 he made an offer to take over the Ding Dong Syndicate and operate as a part of his group, Gwinear Tin Mines Ltd, but the Ding Dong shareholders declined the offer, preferring to resume working as an independent concern. The latter restarted the plant in March 1920, a disastrous year for Cornish mining as it was the onset of another slump in tin prices.

In February, at the beginning of the crash, tin was £396 per ton, falling to £213 by the end of the year and then to £156 per ton by the succeeding March. The company soon realised that under the prevailing conditions it could not hope to make a profit, and in May, after only three months of working, operations ceased for good. John Penberthy gave up his directorship and left Cornwall, and four years later the remaining directors resigned as a body when the company was taken over by Gwinear Tin Mines Ltd.[16]

Calvert took over the property in April 1924 and immediately the new company began exploratory work at Treen Downs, one mile NNE of Ding Dong. In

THE

DING DONG TIN MINES, Ltd.

(Incorporated under the Companies Acts, 1908–1917.)

AUTHORISED CAPITAL - £100,000

Divided into 400,000 Ordinary Shares of 5s. each.

There will be offered early next week for Subscription at par 320,000 Shares of 5s. each.

Directors.

SIR HENRY MONTAGU ROGERS, J.P., Nansloe, Helston, Cornwall. (Chairman of East Pool and Agar, Ltd., Tehidy Minerals, Limited, and Tolgus Mines, Limited.)

HERBERT SYMONDS GOLDSMITH, C.M.G., of Heatherwode, Buxted, Sussex (late Lieut.-Governor of the Northern Provinces of Nigeria).

JOHN WILLIAMS HORTON BOLITHO, J.P., Penmere, Falmouth, Cornwall. (Director of Pengkalen, Limited, and Tekka-Taiping, Limited.)

CHRISTOPHER GERALD ROWS, 170, Piccadilly, London, W.1, *Engineer*.

Bankers.

MIDLAND BANK LIMITED, 5, Threadneedle Street, and Branches.

Brokers.

MOY, SMITH, VANDERVELL & CO., 20, Copthall Avenue, London, E.C.2, and Stock Exchange.

ABBOTT & WICKETT, Redruth Cornwall.

Consulting Engineers.

LAKE & CURRIE, Broad Street Avenue, Blomfield Street, E.C.2.

Secretary (*pro tem.*) and Registered Offices.

W. E. HOLLIDGE, A.C.I.S., Portland House, 73, Basinghall Street, E.C.2.

The Prospectus will state *inter alia* that the Company has been formed to acquire :—

(*a*) The well-known Ding Dong Mine, having an area of 504 acres, situated in the Parish of Gulval, near Penzance, in the Land's End mineral division, held on a Lease or Sett for 42 years from 24th June, 1925, at the yearly rent of £60.

(*b*) The Treen or Treen Down property, in the parish of Zennor, about one mile East of the Ding Dong Mine, having an area of 64 acres, held on a Lease or Sett for 42 years from 23rd February, 1925, at the yearly rent of £10.

(*c*) A large quantity of dumps on the Ding Dong property, some of which have been worked in recent years, and over 13,600 tons during the period September, 1912, to March, 1925, were picked, yielding about 8 lb. of black tin concentrates per ton.

A feature of the Mines is that, owing to their situation in a granite formation they are comparatively free from water and are known locally as "dry" mines. The cables of the Cornwall Electric Power Company pass close to the Ding Dong Company.

The property was originally owned by some of the leading men in Cornwall, and was managed in the latter period of its operations by the old and well-known Cornish firm of Messrs. T. Bolitho and Sons. The books kept by that firm show that during the last twenty-eight years in which the Mines were operated by the crude and old-fashioned methods then in use they yielded 3,472 tons of Black Tin concentrates, realizing a total of £225,162, or an average of £64 10s. per ton. Operations were suspended in 1878 chiefly owing to the fact that the price of Metallic Tin had fallen to £36 per ton.

The properties have been examined by the well-known Consulting Engineers, Messrs. Lake and Currie, of London, who conclude their report by stating :—

"We have every reason to anticipate that the development work suggested will result in the opening up of large ore reserves, not only in connection with the extension of the lodes previously exploited, but also in the discovery of additional ones in the unexplored portions of the properties."

It is the intention of the board to give effect to the recommendations of Messrs. Lake and Currie, and to allocate £50,000 of the capital now issued to the necessary plant, machinery, mining operations, and working capital.

The approximate annual profits, after allowing for Smelting Charges, Royalties, etc., and taking all-in working costs, exclusive of administration, at 27s. per ton of ore raised and treated, are estimated as follows :—

			£
Metallic Tin at £200 per ton	.	22,000
,, ,, £250 ,,	.	34,000
,, ,, £280 ,,	.	41,000

With a recovery of 50 lb. per ton of ore, the annual output would be approximately 330 tons, and the approximate annual profits :—

				£
With Metallic Tin at £200 per ton	.	14,000
,, ,, ,, £250 ,,	.	24,000
,, ,, ,, £280 ,,	.	30,000

The amount required to pay a dividend of 10 per cent. on this issue of Shares is £8,000.

Copies of the full Prospectus will be obtainable on and after Friday, 15th October, from the Company's Bankers, Midland Bank, Limited, 5, Threadneedle Street, London, E.C.2, and Branches ; from the Brokers, Messrs. Moy, Smith, Vandervell and Co., 20, Copthall Avenue, London, E.C.2, and Messrs. Abbott and Wickett, Redruth, Cornwall ; and from the Portal Trust and Agency, Limited, Portland House, Basinghall Street, London, E.C.2.

1924 prospectus for South Ding Dong Mine.

**Outcrop workings on Bossiliack Lode, with
Greenburrow in the background.** *Tony Clarke.*

**Small shafts and outcrop workings on Bussa Lode,
with Greenburrow in the background.** *Tony Clarke.*

167

Two views of the Greenburrow engine house including roof timbers. *Tony Clark.*

168

May it commenced sinking a shaft (at SW 447 363) in what was described as "new ground", but numerous costeaning pits in the area clearly indicate that the ground had previously been worked, although it is not known when. The shaft eventually reached a depth of 40 feet but exceptionally hard ground was encountered. That, combined with excessive water, caused the project to be abandoned and no further work was done in any part of Ding Dong by Gwinear Tin Mines.[17] In 1925 the company was voluntarily wound up and Harold Evens, of No. 1 Gresham Buildings, London E. C., was appointed as liquidator and in addition was authorised to consent to the registration of a new company under the name of Ding Dong Mines Ltd.

While Gwinear Tin Mines was preparing to be wound up it seems that even more plans were afoot to continue working the sett and a report was produced by Messrs Lake and Currie, of whom nothing else is known, in October 1924.[18] The report stated that the sett covered 504 acres and was currently under a 21-year lease at a yearly rental of £60 which would merge into dues of 1-30th of the gross value of "all the tin ore and/or other minerals raised, exclusive of china clay and china stone for which a separate lease is being obtained". An estimate of previous production was given at 3,472 tons of black tin during the period 1850-78 which realised £222,162. There being no definitive information it was estimated "from the number of stamps employed and allowing for the crude methods of treatment then in vogue" that the ore ran at 3-4% tin, *i.e.* 66-88lbs of black tin per ton. It was also estimated that there were on the order of nine miles of levels between the adit and 80-fathom level and a further one mile below this. The dumps were extensive and during the period September 1912 to March 1915 some 13,648 tons of picked ore had been treated, producing over 51 tons of black tin from an average grade of 8lbs per ton. It was considered that another 30,000 tons of dump material were still available although this could not be verified because the dumps were overgrown.

The possibility of china clay extraction was also mooted. This material had been discovered in the north-west part of the set and prospected by sinking a number of test pits to depths of between 8 and 24 feet over an area of 68,000 square feet. With only one exception the pits had encountered good quality clay.

Continuing with the operations would require deepening the sump shaft (presumably Greenburrow although Tredinnick was the deepest) below the present 86 fathoms (below adit) to unwater the mine. This would provide access to the main workings, which were around 80 fathoms deep and a crosscut driven to explore New Lode, which had been barely touched in previous operations. It was also recommended that a new shaft be sunk in the north east part of the sett to explore the ground between Standard and Robin's lodes. The report also mentions Treen Downs to the north, although this appears to be unconnected with the Ding Dong project.

The working capital of the new operation was estimated at £50,000, of which £24,000 was for the plant and machinery and £26,000 for the mining operations. The profits were based on several assumptions:

> The mill to treat 50 tons per day
> Recovery levels of 75lb/ton
> Tin content of 65%
> 300 days milling per year
> Total working costs of 27s per ton
> Market value of the product of £200

One ton of concentrate, minus smelters' charges, royalties, etc would be £110 and working costs of £40, giving a profit of £70/ton. Assuming the production of 500 tons per annum this would give a profit of £35,000 per annum exclusive of "London office charges", ever the burden of Cornish mines. A caveat given was that the average values of the crude ore were considerably higher than the Cornish average and this would have seriously over-estimated the recovery and profits. It is not known if this report was responsible for the appearance of a new prospectus in October 1926 but before any further development work could take place there was another slump in tin prices and the company was dissolved, the final notice of its dissolution appearing nearly four years later in the *London Gazette*, dated March 18th 1930.[19]

Chapter 10 References

1. *The Cornishman* 17.6.1880
2. There is a return of 2 cwt. of black tin given for 1906 at Treen Downs which

was being worked by 'Dan M. Thomas and Party'. Four men were employed underground.

3. William A. Morris, 1988. The Ding Dong Mining Syndicate 1911-1925, *Journal of the Trevithick Society* no.15, 1988, pp68-74

4. *The Cornishman* 12.12.1912 and Morris - op cit.

5. Information per Clive Carter

6. Morris, W. A., 1988, *op. cit.*

7. *The Cornishman* 11.1.1915

8. Cornwall Record Office document WH/1/4530

9. *The Cornishman* 12.12.1912 and Morris - op. cit. p70

10. *The Cornishman* 11.1.1913

11. Morris, W. A., 1988, *op. cit.*p70

12. *The Cornishman* 11.1.1913

13. *The Cornishman* 7.4.1914

14. *The Cornishman* 18.6.1914

15. Morris, W. A., 1988, *op. cit.*p11

16. Morris, W. A., 1988, *op. cit.*and *The Cornishman* 27.4.1916

17. *The Cornishman* 14.5.1924

18. Cornwall Record Office document 14a DDX 104/17

19. Morris, W. A., 1988, *op. cit.*p74

Chapter 11

Final attempts

In 1948 the Cornish Mining Development Association was formed. This was a body devoted to furthering the possibilities of a permanent revival in Cornish mining and, in the ensuing years, with a steady increase in the price of tin, there was a reawakening of interest in the economic potential of mining districts throughout the county. The boom of renewed speculation came in the early 1960s and by 1964 prospecting was being carried out on about twenty properties, ranging from Kit Hill, to Breage and St Ives. In the latter area attention was first directed on the Carnelloe Mine, situated on the cliffs near Zennor. Here three applications had been made to re-open the mine, two by William Thomas Harry of Penzance, and one by Consolidated Gold Fields, and each time the proposals met with fierce opposition. Carnelloe was not reopened.

In March 1965, Giew Mine near Cripples Ease was being investigated by Baltrink Ltd, which was formed by Westfield Minerals Ltd. of Canada,[1] and by April diamond drilling was in progress on the northern flank of Trink Hill in order to prove the eastern extension of the Giew lodes. In all twelve holes were drilled which proved the presence of three to five lodes, but a large crosscourse was encountered and this greatly complicated the interpretation of the results. Also the company was unable to discover the owners of the mineral rights in a vital part of the mine and in June the venture was abandoned.[2]

Early in 1966 *The Cornishman* reported that an application to mine for tin at Ding Dong, using open-cast methods, was to come before the March meeting of the Cornwall County Planning Committee. The actual area to be worked was said to be about 1,000 acres stretching about a quarter of a mile south of Carn Galver, to a quarter of a mile north-east of Bosworthen Farm, which is about a mile due north of Trengwainton Carn, and in the other direction, from Lanyon Farm to Newmill.[3]

The company behind this latest proposal was the Cyprus Mines Corporation, and their proposals for excavating a large area of moorland met with a great deal of hostility. Opposition to the scheme came from all sides, from antiquarians and conservationists, one being Jaquetta Hawkes, archaeologist and wife of the writer J. B. Priestley.[4] Speaking at a meeting of the Federation of Old Cornwall Societies in March, the Cornish miming historian A. K. Hamilton Jenkin, who had previously seconded a resolution opposing opencast mining at Ding Dong, warned that if there were too many objections, there would be the risk of the overseas corporation losing patience with a Cornwall which did nothing but raise objections. "If that happens", he declared, "Cornwall will never get a chance again", and added, "I would not like it thought the Old Cornwall movement is opposed to mining in principle or to the mining of tin by methods other than open-cast. Personally I think we are taking a very grave risk in Cornwall by putting too many restrictions on the people who are genuinely trying to develop mines for the winning of tin". Commenting on the opposing of another proposed venture, namely the dredging of St Ives Bay for tin, he said, "I thought the remark that dredging would deprive the St Ives bathing beaches of their sand was most foolish. I can remember Porthminster beach being stripped of sand in one night, and one had the pathetic and ridiculous sight of St Ives Council having carts of sand being brought from Porthmeor beach to be put on Porthminster. Not a scrap of sand remained after the next tide, and yet three days later the sand was all back on the beach", and he added "Anything that man can do in the way of dredging, relatively far out, is nothing to what nature might do in a day or night in a matter of hours".

Further criticism of opponents of the Ding Dong scheme came from Leonard Thomas, then the Chairman of Geevor Tin Mines, who at a meeting of the Camborne and Redruth Chamber of Commerce, commented on the numerous "bearded weirdies" who objected to all new mining development, and went on to explain the tremendous contribution mining was making and could make to the county's economy. He concluded by stating that it was the duty of the mining engineer to encourage exploitation of the natural wealth that

God had given us, and added, "We cannot put a factory down just where we would like to. We have to go where the mineral is. A lot of bearded weirdies who oppose us are exceptionally ill-informed about what goes on in opening a new mine".[5] However, hostility to the project continued to mount from all parties, hirsute or otherwise, and public opinion won the day. The Cyprus Mines Corporation withdrew its application and the matter was dropped, but not for long as a year later Ding Dong was in the news again. This time it was Consolidated Goldfields Ltd. which, at the end of May 1967, notified F. V. Rolfe, the Western Area Planning Officer, that the company proposed to carry out prospecting at Ding Dong Mine, with a view to reopening it if the results were favourable,[6] Although in that case it had been decided to employ conventional methods of working rather than open-cast mining the scheme, like its predecessor, succumbed to public opinion and was also abandoned.

Eighteen years later the final storm erupted when in June 1985 Geevor Tin Mines proposed removing material from the dumps at Ding Dong and transporting it back to the mill for treatment (Geevor had already started to remove material from various parts of the St Just area, for example Wheal Cock and Wheal Bal). The areas to be worked were around Greenburrow, Bolitho's and Providence shafts – a total of just under four acres,[7] but nothing ensued from this plan as shortly afterwards the sudden crash of world tin prices precipitated the Tin Crisis and, ultimately, the end of Cornish tin mining.

Chapter 11 References

1. *The Cornishman* 2.6.1965
2. Trounson, J. H., 1993. *Areas in Cornwall of Mineral Potential*, University of Exeter Press, pp15-17
3. *The Cornishman* 17.2.1966
4. *The Cornishman* 24.2.1966 and 26.5.1966
5. *The Cornishman* 10.3.1966
6. *The Cornishman* 1.6.1967
7. *The Cornishman* 29.8.1988

Chapter 12

South Ding Dong Mine

South Ding Dong Mine lies about half a mile south-south-east of Ding Dong Mine and a quarter of a mile southwest of Carfury chapel. The 25-inch Ordnance Survey map of 1880 shows a shaft in the valley (SW 443 339) about 100 yards west of the Chyandour Stream, about 250 yards north-east of Mount Whistle.

The mine had been working prior to 1839 and was advertised for sale ("all that promising mine") in April that year.[1] It was not worked on a very extensive scale as only one horse whim was advertised.

The mine was working again in the 1850s and in 1854 materials to the value of £3 were purchased by Ding Dong Mine.[2] In the following year a reply to a correspondent in the *Mining Journal* stated that the concern had no London office, but that James Permewan was believed to be the purser.[3] What transpired regarding actual mining operations at this stage is not known, if indeed any were carried out at all under the watchful eye of Mr Permewan, as that worthy gentleman was then busily engaged in 'cooking the books' at the East and North Ding Dong Mining Companies where he also held the office of purser.[4]

A series of reports was issued with the prospectus for South Ding Dong in late 1858 or early 1859.[5] The report for February 1858, from Thomas Harvey, "Mining Agent", stated that a shaft had been sunk four fathoms on a lode parallel to those of Ding Dong. The lode was described as being two feet wide, producing 5cwt of tin per 100 barrows of 22 gallons. The shaft had been abandoned through problems with water. Following this an adit had been

Sale advertisement from the *West Briton*, 25.4.1839

driven 90 fathoms on a caunter lode, which produced some tin. At the time of writing the adit was 10-12 fathoms away from the abandoned shaft; the adit would presumably drain the shaft. In driving another six or eight fathoms the Union Lode would be reached, on which tin had already been broken. On one of the Standard lodes a shaft had been sunk nine fathoms, the lode being three feet wide. This lode was also producing 5cwt of tin per 100 barrows.

A postscript to the report adds:

> The late Adventurers were a small party residing in the Neighbourhood of the Mine, some of whom in the time of the Gold fever emigrated to Australia, and the remainder were not strong enough to carry on the Mine, and so it became abandoned.

A larger report was issued for September 1858, by Richard Grenfell of Madron. This also mentions the four fathom deep shaft, though oddly states that the ore produced was "100 bushels of 22 gallons bushel". Grenfell had apparently dialled the level and determined that the end was only 12 fathoms from the shaft. The price for driving the level would be £3 per fathom, the lode having been identified as the Clukey Lode of Ding Dong. driving the adit 50 fathoms on the Union Lode would intersect another four lodes, at which point the adit would be 30 fathoms deep. The first of these was the Wig Lode, then two east-west lodes and finally Buzza Lode. The two named lodes had "produced Tens of Thousands Pounds worth of Tin" in Ding Dong, an optimistic statement if ever one was ever written! Grenfell believed that, based on pumping at Ding Dong, an engine of 18 or 20 inches diameter would be sufficient to "prove the whole of the lodes".

The report for February 1859 was by Richard Taylor, of Ludgvan. Taylor had little to say about the mine, though it did state that

> This place was worked some time by a party of Miners from the Neighbourhood, who expended several pounds in executing various operations, especially in driving an Adit to cut lodes at a deeper level, but their Capital being so very limited, they could do no more, & thus they were compelled to abandon their enterprise before reaching the object contemplated.

The report is so general that one wonders if Taylor actually knew anything about the mine, let alone having visited it. The new company was formed with a capital of £2,000 in 100 £2 shares, the deposit to be 10s per share.[6] The sett was in the manor of Boswarthen and had been granted by Sir R. R. Vyvyan and Edmund Davey at 1/18th dues, reduced to 1/20th after the erection of a steam engine.

The sett was said to extend for about three quarters of a square mile and was

SOUTH DING DONG.

CAPITAL £2,000

IN 1,000 SHARES OF £2 PER SHARE, DEPOSIT 10s. PER SHARE;

TO BE CONDUCTED ON THE COST BOOK SYSTEM.

The Committee of Management to be selected from the Body of Shareholders at their first Meeting.

In presenting to the Public the Prospectus of a Mine of this importance, it will only be necessary to point out its locality, to convince those who are desirous to embark in a Mining speculation, of the success likely to attend it. This valuable Mine is situated in the Manor of Boswarthen, in the Parish of Madron, within two miles of Penzance, where all Materials necessary for Mining can be obtained at the cheapest rate, and at a trifling expense for carriage. The Sett has been granted by Sir R. R. Vyvyan and Edmund Davey, Esq., at the moderate Dues of 1/18th part: and after the erection of a Steam Engine, of 1/20th part; and extends for about 3/4th of a square Mile.

On reference to the Plan accompanying this Prospectus, it will be seen that SOUTH DING DONG is bounded on the north by the celebrated DING DONG, one of the richest, and by far the oldest Tin Mine in the County, it having returned immense sums to the Shareholders, and the lodes which proved so productive there at a very shallow depth, run into this Sett, upon one of the Lodes called *Bukka* or *Flukey* which traverses the whole length of the Sett, a Steam Engine has lately been erected in Ding Dong to develope its resources at a deeper level.

Part of the prospectus for the new South Ding Dong company.

traversed by the Bukka and Flukey Lodes of Ding Dong, which also bounded South Ding Dong on the north.[7] A considerable amount of money had already been spent on the property; £300 of the mine's capital would be allowed to the present owners, leaving £1,700 for future operations. Applications for shares, of which a "great many" had already been taken up, were to be made to Captain Prince of Redruth.

By May an air shaft was being cleared up and driving operations on an adit, driven for 9 fathoms by the former workers, resumed.[8] In the following month a report in the *Mining Journal* stated that since the commencement of operations, an air shaft, 8 fathoms 3 feet deep, had been sunk to the back of the adit level for the purpose of forcing air into the latter in order to expedite driving the end towards the lodes.[9] In June 1860 the mine acquired 'a small air machine for blowing air down the shaft', presumably to expedite driving the adit.[10] This work having been completed, the end was set to drive 10 fathoms by a pare or men at £4 per fathom, and to cut the Bucca Lode of Ding Dong Mine on which 4 fathoms 3 feet had already been driven.

In January 1861 the balance in favour of the shareholders was £10 4s 2d. Several shafts were said to have been cleared up and two of them had been sunk on North and South Standard lodes. The lodes, which could vary from six inches to three feet in width, both underlay north and both were producing a small quantity of ore of good quality. They were described as looking favourable to become more productive at greater depth. The accounts were accepted and a call of 2s 6d per share was made.[11]

The Appendix to the *UK Mineral Statistics* for 1861 gives John Prince[12] as the purser and manager while the same publication for 1864 lists the mine as "suspended".

Chapter 12 References

1. *West Briton* 25.4.1839
2. Cost Book at RIC (notes per Justin Brooke)
3. *Mining Journal* 28.4.1855
4. For a full account of Permewan's activities see *Stannary Tales* by Justin Brooke, pp64-66

5. Cornwall Record Office document DDM 252/36: South Ding Dong Mine prospectus

6. Cornwall Record Office document DDM 252/36: South Ding Dong Mine prospectus

7. *Mining Journal* 11.2.1860

8. *Mining Journal* 19.5 1860

9. *Mining Journal* 23.6.1860

10. Information per Clive Carter

11. *Cornish Telegraph* 16.1.1861

12. John Prince had worked as an agent to various mines, including Sark's Hope Silver Mine in the Channel Islands.

Chapter 13

East Ding Dong Mine

East Ding Dong Mine was situated on the south-eastern slopes of Mulfra Hill, about one mile ENE of Ding Dong Mine, extending to the south through Ninnis to Bay of Biscay, near Newmill. Originally the sett was worked as Mulfra Hill Mine and was active in the first decade of the 18th century. On the 9th of May 1709 a tinner by the name of George Roach received the sum of thirty shillings from the Hon. S. William Godolphin in payment of toll tin "made and broaken in Mulfra within the parish of Maddern"[1] and in 1768 the mine owed the sum of 6s 4d to the bankrupt William John, formerly a merchant of Penzance.[2] It is not known when this working ceased. The mine was next worked in the 1830s, leaving an undocumented period of some 68 years. However, it is not unreasonable to suppose that further work was carried on during this period.

Under the name of East Ding Dong the mine was re-started in 1836. Four fifths of the shares in the company were acquired by the Mount's Bay Mining Company, and the remaining fifth was taken up by proprietors in Cornwall and Devon. The mine was divided into 100 shares, some of which, presumably the remaining 20%, were advertised for sale in July of that year[3] and more in August.[4]

In November 1836 a report on the mine was given in the *Mining Journal*.[5] The mine was now operating under the auspices of the Mounts Bay Silver-Lead, Copper and Tin Mines, shares for which had been advertised by the secretary, C. R. Roberts, in January that year.[6] The report had been some time in coming, the writer stating "I have refrained from giving any public report in these mines until such time as I can speak with some degree of confidence". The set was about a mile in length and width, and known to contain upwards of fifteen lodes. The mine lay between Wheal Reeth and Ding Dong, mines which had "yielded the proprietors immense profits, and are still very rich". The agent had worked in one of the mines (probably Ding Dong) as a miner for over ten years and as an agent for six years in the other. He considered the set "likely to make as good a mine as either of the above-named mines".

The sett was described as being several (that is, an undivided property). This the owner had caused to be done "in consequence of some persons having reported that I had not a good title to the set". He had receipts from eight-tenths of the lords, and the whole of the bounder's right through the undivided common of Mulfra Hill and Ninnis.

Much work had been carried out since the mine had reopened. It had been cleared to 35 fathoms from surface, and 10 fathoms below adit. The lode was nearly perpendicular, about 3½ feet wide, "containing good work, averaging from eight to ten feet per balcon"; the adit had been driven 200 fathoms on the lode. In places, the "ancients" had sunk winzes on the richer parts of the lode.

It was thought that two caunter lodes would be cut twenty fathoms beyond the present end and in cross-cutting and "cross-turning" another three lodes had been cut; the latter promised to be productive as they were parallel lodes. The adit had been driven 30 fathoms west of the present shaft by the ancients and this would provide 40 fathoms of backs to be stoped. The main lode was 3 to 4 feet wide, from which large quantities of ore had been returned; a winze had been sunk below the adit to an unknown depth. Even though half of the lode had been taken down, the remainder would pay for working at the current price of tin.

The main lode would keep an eight-head stamps constantly at work, as soon as it could be erected, from pitches that could be set at once. The lode in the shaft improved with depth; this was an advantage as there was little water in the mine, the present whim apparently the first erected on this mine. A parcel of ore had been sampled the previous week, and was valued at over £53, enough to pay the dues to eight-tenths of the lords and bounder.

In 1839 an independent description of the mine from 1836 stated: There is a small undertaking in Mulfra Hill, called the "East Ding Dong Mine," which recommenced in 1836; there is no steam-engine, and about 15 men are employed in the concern.[7]

Later in the month work had commenced building the smiths' shop and count house, which were nearly finished.[8] Once that had been done work would start on the stamps. The lode was still improving and the ends were being driven east and west. The tinstuff was worth 6s to 7s per barrow and enough ore was available to keep "an eight head-stamps constantly at work for twelve months". In addition about 600 kibbles of stuff was at grass, presumably on the sumps, thrown away by the ancients and worth 4s per barrow. One pair of stamps could stamp about £250 worth of ores per month, leaving 30% profit; the stream running through the sett could, however, drive three pairs of stamps.

The report for Christmas Eve stated that a good course of tin, 20 inches wide, had been discovered in the winze under the adit, about 25 fathoms east of the "main working shaft".[9] The writer, Edward Thomas, was able to wax lyrical about this:

> Considering the very great extent of this set, the strata, end the great number of lodes, every experienced miner must conclude that this mine presents a speculation of the first interest. The strata and the prospects of the lodes, are equally so good at the same depth as those very rich mines in this district, as Old Ding Dong and Wheal Reeth, which has given the adventurers a clear profit of 190,000/. within the last few years. It is my decided opinion, soon after the stamps are erected, and the necessary work done, there will be such quantities of tin brought to market, that will in a short time pay a great dividend. I would also impress on your mind, that from the great number of known lodes in this set, it may fairly be stated, that this mine is of the first consequence as to durability. I conclude by stating that this mine presents brilliant prospects.

Two weeks later the winze had been cleared, it was 7 fathoms deep, and the course of tin found to be 18 to 20 fathoms in length, dipping steeply to the west.[10] There were 7 to 12 fathoms of backs to work for as little as 6s or 7s in the pound; it was only the lack of stamps that prevented the mine making a profit. At surface there was £200 worth of ores while a pair of men were stoping the west end of the eastern winze on "an excellent course of tin".

A general meeting of the shareholders of the company was held at the offices, 35, Seething-lane, on Monday, May 7th, chaired by Joseph Gray.[11] Mr (or Captain) Bennetts, the manager, was asked to read various reports on the mine and to detail the "real prospects" of the company. It was then proposed, and carried unanimously, "That Messrs. Gray and Armitage be deputed to proceed to Cornwall forthwith to inspect the mines and audit the accounts, preparatory to their furnishing a report to a general meeting of shareholders, to be held on the 25th of June next, in pursuance of a specific resolution then passed, to receive the same, and for the transaction of other business connected with the company."

The reasons behind this were not stated, however the Secretary then called attention to the fact that he had received several anonymous letters "tending to create a dissension in the management". A second resolution was then passed to Messrs Bennetts and Roberts, "expressive of the approbation and entire satisfaction of the meeting in the management of the affairs of the company". One attendee, a Mr Foster, had represented shareholders in Liverpool and Manchester.

At the beginning of November 1837 six heads of stamps were at work, stamping the old men's leavings, which had been taken some months prior from the levels in clearing up the mine.[12] The inferior (lower grade) work was stamped first in order to reduce the tin lost in the process; this would take three or four weeks to do. Once this was finished work would start on ore from the mine. Tributers had taken the backs of some old workings at 10s in the pound, while a new shaft was being sunk near the water-engine (water wheel) so that flat rods could be used for pumping.

A week later it was reported that another large parallel lode had been discovered in the new shaft.[13] This was nearly 3 feet wide and rich in tin likely to be very productive in depth. This was regarded as one of the "very rich and productive lodes in the Great Ding Dong (which is the oldest mine on record in the county of Cornwall), and still yielding very large profits to the proprietors". All of the standard lodes in Ding Dong were said to run through East Ding Dong mine for "upwards of a mile in length". The tin in the mine was said to be the "equal in quality to any in the county; the stratum similar in every respect to Ding Dong and Wheal Reeth; the one mine situated to the east and the other due west of us". Of course the lodes in those mines did not reach from one to the other, however Bennetts was being no less enthusiastic than any other agent in a new mine would be, regardless of how incautious his statement really was. Work had started on a burning house, following which a powder house would be built.

By December 11th the new shaft was down to the adit level where there was a good course of tin extending east and west.[14] A ten fathom level was now being driven east and west on a large and kindly lode, where a few fathoms more driving would reach the main ore shoot. Stamping of mine ore had commenced the previous Monday however the machinery was not up to dealing with raising the ore and the agent was looking for a small engine to pump and stamp. The burning house was nearly finished. The report for January 22nd 1838 mentions the new shaft sinking below the adit.[15] The report was actually written by Charles Roberts, the secretary, and perhaps for this reason some of the terminology is a little odd. There was a fine lode in the bottom of the new shaft where "we are come to the bottoms of the old sink-one part was only a few fathoms below the adit". All of the tin stuff was being saved, implying that there was at least some recoverable tin in the ore, while at surface "The stamps are at work, boys hunking and framing slime, pits full". The burning house was now completed and it was hoped to have a 2-ton parcel of ore ready within four weeks. As soon as an engine was at work a large quantity of tin would be raised, however they would not be able to sink much further until the engine had been erected.

In May the lode below the ten fathom level was "very much improved" and improving in the sinking; it was worth 5s per barrow clear profit.[16] It was intended to sink the shaft another ten fathoms and drive a level into the ore shoot, at which point the number of tributers would be increased. One pare was working at 2s 6d in the pound; they had broken £40 worth of tin the previous month at a cost of 5s. It was proposed to sink the deepest shaft, only 37 fathoms from surface, another 20 fathoms. At this point crosscuts would be driven north and south to intersect six other parallel lodes which were being worked in Ding Dong.

A meeting of the company was held at the King's Arms, Holborn Bridge, on December 15th, attended by many of the principal shareholders.[17] A Captain Thomas corroborated Captain Bennetts' opinion and prospects of the mine and also explained that as the lodes in Ding Dong Mine were very rich, they would also be rich in East Ding Dong. However a steam engine would be necessary so that "large returns would be the result in a few months". There is no evidence however that the shareholders were happy to go along with him.

The next report was from December 1838, though it actually reported very little.[18] At Bennetts' Shaft there was a "kindly, fine lode, in a beautiful strata" but without any tin to comment on. In October, two young men had been put to work driving on a north and south lode about 250 fathoms north of the main workings. Here an east-west lode had been cut 5 fathoms from surface and "I never saw a lode possessing finer properties at the same depth". Fifteen fathoms beyond the present end here was another east-west lode; these "discoveries will, of course, enhance the value of the mine materially. The Old Ding Dong is now as she has been for many years, very rich. We also shall have a good mine in depth".

Another general meeting of the shareholders in this company was held at the King's Arms Inn, on June 14th.[19] This was for the purpose of receiving the report of a committee which had appointed at a previous meeting to investigate the accounts. Unfortunately Joseph Gray had to report that, until a day or two prior to the meeting the committee had not seen the secretary's and treasurer's accounts; consequently it was not able to report on them.

However there were many charges "which required strict investigation". A gentleman "well acquainted with mining affairs" was appointed to assist the committee in its investigation. Charles Roberts, the secretary, tendered his resignation at this meeting, which accepted.

On November 13th a decree was made by the Vice-Warden of the Stannaries in the cases of James Polglaze v. Thomas and another and John Polglaze v. same.[20] The decree was that a sale was to be made of tin ores and, if necessary, all of the mine's machinery and materials. The proceeds were to be applied by the Registrar of the Court "in the manner directed by the Decree in the above consolidated causes". Unfortunately it is not known who the principals

Stannary Court decree for the sale of the materials at East Ding Dong; *West Briton*, 29.11.1839

were, though Thomas must have represented the mine; the sale was to take place on December 18th at 11 a.m.

Applications for viewing were to be made to the mine or to Mr Gillson, the plaintiffs' solicitor in Truro. A meeting of shareholders was held at the Kings Arms on December 18th to receive the delayed report on the accounts and other matters.[21] The immediate result of the meeting was to agree to a call of 5s per share.[22] Another meeting was then called for January 16th 1840.[23] At this meeting it was reported that there had been no response to the call.[24] It was also stated that unless immediate steps were taken to procure the necessary funds for the working of East Ding Dong, the mine would probably be lost. It was therefore proposed that:

1. That the shares should be declared forfeited.

2. That a letter should he sent to all the known shareholders.

3. That this meeting be advertised in the [London] *Gazette*, calling upon the shareholders generally to contribute to the fund necessary to be raised for the preservation of the mine and the prosecution of the works, and in default of the shareholders not complying with such resolution within one month from the date of this advertisement, the shareholders be treated as having for ever forfeited their shares, and relinquished all their interest in the mine, without prejudice to all former claims the company may have against such shareholders with respect to the mine,

and all monies expended on the said mine, it being the Intention of those shareholders who may contribute to such fund to work the said mine, and appropriate all profits arising out of the same for their own exclusive benefit and advantage.

A meeting of the shareholders was held at the Star Hotel, Manchester, on the 28th March 1840.[25] It seems likely that this location was chosen as there seems to have been a large proportion of northerners amongst the shareholders. The investigation into the secretary's and treasurer's accounts was completed; both of these positions, and that of company solicitor, had been held by Charles Roberts. "...when a full and particular statement of such accounts, and his charges for salary, &c., were submitted and investigated, when it was resolved:

That the meeting feel exceedingly indignant at Mr Roberts's conduct, in attempting to commit a fraud on the company, by making such exorbitant and extravagant charges, and which they cannot consent to admit or allow.

It was further resolved – That this meeting consider that immediate steps should be taken against Mr Roberts, to compel him to refund such sum or sums of money that he may be indebted to the company, as well to compel him to give up all books, documents, and papers now in his possession belonging to the company (he having tendered his resignation), and that they are ready and willing, in conjunction with the other shareholders, to contribute to the expenses that may be required in taking such steps."

Not surprisingly, a response appeared the following week in the *Mining Journal*:[26]

[ADVERTISEMENT.]
MOUNT'S BAY MINING COMPANY.
TO THE EDITOR OF THE MINING JOURNAL.

SIR,—Having observed in your *Journal* of the 11th inst., an advertisement purporting to be the resolutions of a meeting of this company, held at the Star Hotel, Manchester, on the 28th ult., in which charges of a serious nature are brought against me in my professional character, allow me to request you will insert in your next Number my most positive denial of the truth of the imputation conveyed by the resolutions in question. With regard to the accounts rendered by me, and which were made out by an accountant, by the direction of a meeting of the company, I court the strictest investigation, and shall be ready to hand over any books, documents, or papers in my possession, relating to the company, on being paid my demand. I have also to request you will favour me with the name and address of the author of the advertisement in question, that I may adopt such proceedings as I may be advised with regard to the scandalous charges brought against me.

I am, Sir, your very obedient servant,

Seething-lane, April 16

THOMAS R. ROBERTS.

Unfortunately the *Journal* had got Roberts' first name wrong and an apology appeared the following week.[27]

In December 1840 a man called Richard Nicholas was killed after being struck on the head by a falling stone; he left a widow and seven children. The *Penzance Gazette* reported the accident at East Ding Dong while the *West Briton* gave the old name of Mulfra Hill Mine.[28,29]

The mine, although not actually named, was offered for sale in October 1843:[30]

VALUABLE INVESTMENT

FOR SALE

A VALUABLE TIN MINE

IN CORNWALL WITH

Machinery, Tin Bounds, Mining Setts, Erections, &c. complete.

THE MINING PROPERTY here offered is of considerable extent, and situated in a rich Mining district, adjoining on the East and containing the Lodes of Ding Dong, in the valuable parish of Gulval.

AT THE COST OF £8,000 several valuable LODES have been laid open – SHAFTS have been laid open— SHAFTS have been sunk — WATER COURSES brought in—BOUNDS purchased and an ENGINE and STAMPING MILLS erected (ready to work at a few hours' notice:) The present proprietor wishes to place the concern on the most liberal terms, reserving only a small interest therein, in the bands of any respectable Cornish Company disposed to avail themselves of the great advantages here at a very SMALL OUTLAY.

The SETTS and MATERIALS may be examined, and every information obtained, by applying to Mr. F. J. MANNING, NO. 2 Dyers Buildings, Holborn, London, or Mr. J. F. TREGELLAS, Truro, who is fully authorized to dispose of the property.

London, 17th Oct. 1843.

The sale seems to have been unsuccessful, and the materials were offered for sale in May 1845:[31]

85 fathoms 5-in Capstan rope

Horse Engine, complete

1 Horse Whim

1 Large capstan shieve

30 fathoms 4-in pumps

6-in and 5-in Windbore, cast strong for sinking

24-in   "   "

1 6-in Knee piece, or Jack Head, complete

2 3½-in door pieces

60 fathoms Bristol air pipes

2 pair tapered rod plates, 14′ 6″ by 6″

1 L Bob with carriages, guddeons (gudgeons), etc.

Applications were to be made from either Higgs and Son in Penzance or Captain Penberthy at the Providence Mines, Lelant.

In May and June 1847 Mulfra Hill and Bosulval Tin Mine was offered for sale by private contract.[32,33] The sett was offered "with the WATER-ENGINE, and other MATERIALS necessary for working"; these had apparently not been sold off in 1843. Applications were to be made to Henry Thomas, Lombard Street, London or to Captain Isaac Penberthy, of the Providence Mines, St Ives.

By the end of 1851 the mine was working again, and a call of 10s per share made.[34] The first report on the mine was made by "Subscriber" of Penzance, who was a shareholder:[35]

EAST DING DONG (IN MADRON AND GULVAL).

SIR,—Seeing from the reports of this mine that shares were at a premium, I took it upon myself this afternoon to visit the sett, and beg to hand you the result of my personal inspection and inquiry. The engine-shaft, as left by the former workers, is thought to be about 18 fms. from the surface, and only commenced a renewal of sinking yesterday, which must progress slowly on account of the quickness of water. There was another shaft left by the former workers, about 16 or 18 fms. deep, and about 200 fms, from the present sump, and it is from the supposed lodes in this the shareholders and public are, I believe, led to form wonderful expectations; but I found this shaft full of water, and the imaginary lodes in it never yet to have been seen by the present workers. This shaft can be forked only by means of steam power, aided, from the intended site of the engine-house, by the additional expense of flat-rods. I learn that there are but three lodes in the sett, to one of which the name of the "Bay of Biscay" has been attached, and which is lauded as presenting amazing prospects.

I would certainly recommend to parties about speculating in it, first to obtain the opinion or report of some competent and respectable Cornish captain, as to the feasibility and integrity of the adventurer—
SUBSCRIBER: Penzance, Dec. 7.

A reply to this appeared the following week, penned by John Richards junior, of Penzance.[36] He stated that the sett was secured after "necessary and proper examination by ourselves, aided by disinterested practical men". The mine was divided into 1,024 shares of which 100 were taken by Richards and another 100 by R. R. Michell of Marazion. Using their influence, but "excluding all mere jobbing men" they sold all of the shares. One shareholder wanted to sell some and these (75) were taken by James Permewan, the purser, and sold immediately for a premium of 15s each. Work was being carried out at surface and an efficient steam engine was being built by Harvey & Co.

The *Mining Journal* had received several similar responses and thought that the mine, being managed by Captain White "is satisfactory as to the operations being carried on with judgment and economy".

Two weeks later it was reported that the account house and shops were nearly finished while the engine house and stack had been taken to build for £40, plus £20 for carriage of stone.[37] The 24-inch engine would be built and delivered for £600 and was expected to be at work by March 1st.

Accounts were given in the *Cornish Telegraph* in May 1853:[38]

Labour cost for October 1852	£83 7s 3d
Labour cost for November	£72 5s 4d
Labour cost for December	£74 15s 1d
Labour cost for January 1853	£87 6s 4d
Labour cost for February	£76 6s 9d
Total	£394 0s 9d
Merchants' bills	£424 13s 5d
Credit	£818 13s 5d
By a Call made 21st October 1852 on 1024 shares, at 10s per share	£512 0s 0d
Balance due Purser	£306 18s 5d

It was resolved that a call of 15s per share be made "to pay off the above balance, and for the further prosecution of the mine". The accounts for the period to September 21st showed another adverse balance, this one of £904 8s 2d, including £600 for the engine; to meet this a call of 25s per share was made.[39] Despite this it was decided to raise Permewan's salary to four guineas per month. Captains White and Boyns reported that the lode in Evans's Shaft was 1 to 2 feet wide and very promising. It was hoped to have the flat-rods at working in Twinberrow's Shaft in a fortnight.

At the end of November the engine shaft was being sunk by nine men, and the 16 fm. level was being driven east and west of the shaft.[40] The flat rods were at work at Twinberrow's Shaft, which was cleared to its bottom, and the adit was now driving east. A stamps had been taken, probably Gear Stamps, just

SE of Newmill. The accounts for the end of the year showed another adverse balance and a call of 8s was made.[41] The lode under the 16 fathom level was poor and it was considered that this was not the lode previously worked; consequently the shaft sinking was suspended until that point was proven.

Unfortunately the next accounts showed yet another balance against the mine, of £226 5s 4d, and this was to be "divided pro rata amongst the shareholders, and paid forthwith".[42]

East Ding Dong, in the person of its purser, James Permewan, was included in a letter published on 12th August, from a person signing himself "R" (see North Ding Dong for more information).[43] The claims in the letter were refuted in a letter from various shareholders the following week:

> EAST DING DONG MINE.—SIR: A writer in your Journal, of the 12th inst., signed "R." states that matters are not in a very satisfactory state in this mine, with regard to the purser. Now, Sir, as shareholders residing in the neighbourhood of the mine, we beg to give our most unqualified contradiction to such insinuations, and likewise to state the very great satisfaction the purser has always given the shareholders in every department in connection with this mine. Several of our brother shareholders in London can confirm this, from their personal visits to the mine on the account days and other times.—William Ball, Francis Boase, Francis Trounson, Alfred Chenhalls, Harvey & Co., of Hayle, join in the above. Aug. 16.

The accounts to the end of August showed yet another adverse balance, to be fixed by yet another call, this one of 5s per share.[44] Captains Matthew White and William Boyns reported that the lode in the 10 fathom level was worth £10 per fathom and that a continuation of the lode would enable them to pay the cost of working (£100 per month) in two or three months. The mine was currently raising from £50 to £60 per month. The accounts to the end of November showed:[45]

Balance last account:	£111 6s 10d
Mine cost, Sept. to Nov.:	£263 5s 9d
Merchants' bills:	£133 11s 6d

Total:	£508 4s 1d
Calls received:	£243 10s 0d
Tin sold (less 1-18th dues),	£65 04s 0d
Total	£308 14s 0d
Balance:	-£199 10s 1d

To meet the deficit a call of 6s per share was made. Captain Matthew White reported that in the 10 fathom level, which was driven 16 fathoms east of Twinberrow's Shaft, the lode had been from 1 to 2 feet wide, and had produced some good tinstuff; in the present end it was 14 inches wide, all saving work.

Presumably as a result of this, the mine was advertised for sale in March:[46]

MINING MACHINERY AND MATERIALS FOR SALE.

MR. JAMES PERMEWAN WILL SELL, BY AUCTION, on Tuesday, the 18th day of March next, at Eleven o'clock in forenoon, at EAST DING DONG MINE, in the parish of Madron, 2½ miles from. Penzance, the following valuable MINE MATERIALS, &c.:—viz., A 24 in. cylinder PUMPING ENGINE. 9 ft. stroke in the cylinder, and 8 ft. in the shaft, with wrought-iron boiler, weighing about 8 tons, all new within two years. Capstan and shears; 60 fathoms 9-16in. capstan chain; 3 balance-bobs, complete; 2 8 inch top doorpieces; 2 8 inch windbores; 8 9ft. 9in. pumps; 11 1ft. 8in. working-barrel; 9 ft. 8in. ditto; 5in. top doorpiece; 9ft. 5in. working-barrel; 9ft. 5in. windbore; 6 9ft. 6in. pumps; horse, whim; 80 fms. ½in. whim chain; 100 fms. 1½in. iron flat-rods; 100 fathoms 1½in. ditto; 35 18in. sheaves; 4 8in. buckets and prongs; 2 fms. of pin chain; 9 triple blocks, to carry 9-16 in. chain; 1ft fms. of ladders; 6 dozen 1½in. bolts and burs; 4 taps and plates; a boring machine; 16 fms. 6in. wood rods, with cheeks and brasses; shaft tackle: 70 fms. 4in. air-pipes; 35 pulley-stands; house winch; bricks; and sundry other articles. The auctioneer begs particularly to call attention to the engine, as it is equal in duty to any in Cornwall of a similar size. For viewing apply to the agent on the mine, and for other particulars to the auctioneer, at his mining offices, Penzance.—Dated Feb. 24, 1855.

In April a case as heard in the Penzance County Court, where Captain William

Boyns sued the managing agent, R. Bryon, four guineas for one month's pay.[47] R. Bryon is presumed to be the Robert Byron who was involved in a case regarding James Permewan and North Ding Dong. The case was unsuccessful: the plaintiff was put in the witness box, when, after answering two or three questions with much hesitation, and his evidence being unsatisfactory, judgment was immediately given for defendant, with certain costs.

Despite the sale notice, work was still being carried out at the mine.[48] Since the last account, six men had raised £144 14s 6d worth of tin from the lode in the 10 fathom level at Twinberrow's Shaft. The ground was worth £10 per fathom and it was considered that the six men would break at least £50 worth or tin in the present month. The agents were still trying to put an optimistic view of the mine, finishing "...we have never seen the lode so good at any time since it has been working as at present. If this lode should continue for 20 fms. in length and depth we shall have a good mine". The result of this seems to be that the sale was put back to July 9th.[49]

In May 1857, James Permewan was sued by Sir Henry Onslow, Bart (the High Sheriff of Cornwall) in the Penzance County Court, for the rent of Gear Stamps.[50] The rent, for two years, was only £30, however James Permewan, defending himself, applied for the case to be heard by the Stannaries Court. This was opposed by Mr Cornish (of Rodd, Darke, and Cornish) firstly because the Court had no power to refer the case; and secondly because the case had been partly heard. His Honour did not feel bound to remit every case, some part or the whole of which was connected with mining, to the Stannaries Court, and preferred to hear the case and the defence, and then he would decide whether it ought to be referred. The case therefore proceeded, but "the details were uninteresting". As usual, Permewan was "smartly cross-examined, much to the amusement of the bystanders, and his Honour expressed an

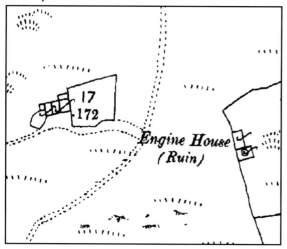

The remains of East Ding Dong as shown on the 1st series Ordnance Survey map.

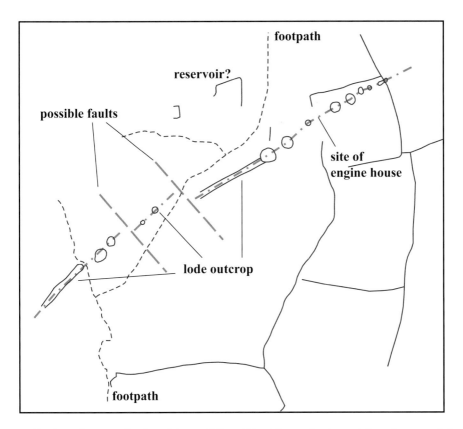

Surface features in the vicinity of East Ding Dong, features taken from aerial photographs.

opinion that the accounts of East Ding Dong, as shown in the cost book, were cooked.—His Honour said he had not the slightest doubt about his judgment—: 21*l*. 4s. 6d., with costs, and immediate payment".

The last reference to the mine appeared in August 1857, a plaintive letter from a shareholder:[51]

EAST DING DONG.—Can any of your readers oblige me by furnishing some information respecting this mine? I relinquished my shares three years ago, and expected at the end of two years to receive the amount due for my proportion of the materials. I have written to the purser several times, but can obtain no satisfactory reply, and my last letter he has not condescended to notice. Any Information respecting the mine which would enable me the better to know my position, and the steps it would be desirable to take, would no doubt be serviceable to other of your readers as well as—An Unfortunate Shareholder: Aug. 21.

References Chapter 13

1. Cornwall Record Office document DD ML 2:1. Malons Records, Receipt for toll of tin from Mulfra Hill 1709
2. Documents per Clive Carter
3. *West Briton* 8 July 1836
4. *West Briton* 12 August 1836
5. *Mining Journal* 10.11.1836
6. *Mining Journal* 2.1.1836 p1
7. Edmunds, R., junior, 1839. *A Statistical Account of the Parish of Madron, containing the Borough of Penzance in Cornwall.* In: Journal of the Statistical Society of London, Volume 2, Charles Knight & Co, London.
8. *Mining Journal* 3.12.1836
9. *Mining Journal* 13.1.1837
10. *Mining Journal* 18.3.1837
11. *Mining Journal* 12.5.1837
12. *Mining Journal* 4.11.1837
13. *Mining Journal* 11.11.1837
14. *Mining Journal* 16.12.1837
15. *Mining Journal* 27.1.1838
16. *Mining Journal* 12.5.1838
17. *Mining Journal* 22.12.1838
18. *Mining Journal* 5.1.1839
19. *Mining Journal* 22.6.1839
20. *West Briton* 29.11.1839
21. *Mining Journal* 7.12.1839
22. *Mining Journal* 21.12.1839
23. *Mining Journal* 11.1.1840
24. *Mining Journal* 18.1.1840
25. *Mining Journal* 11.4.1840
26. *Mining Journal* 18.4.1840
27. *Mining Journal* 25.4.1840

28. *Penzance Gazette* 30.12.1840
29. *West Briton* 1.1.1841
30. *Penzance Gazette* 25.10.1843
31. *Penzance Gazette* 26.5.1845
32. *Mining Journal* 29.5.1847
33. *Mining Journal* 5.6.1847
34. *Mining Journal* 11.1.1852
35. *Mining Journal* 11.12.1852
36. *Mining Journal* 18.12.1852
37. *Mining Journal* 15.1.1853
38. *Cornish Telegraph* 4.5.1853
39. *Mining Journal* 8.10.1853
40. *Mining Journal* 3.12.1853
41. *Mining Journal* 31.12.1853
42. *Mining Journal* 8.4.1854
43. *Mining Journal* 19.8.1854
44. *Mining Journal* 14.10.1854
45. *Mining Journal* 6.1.1855
46. *Mining Journal* 10.3.1855
47. *Mining Journal* 14.4.1855
48. *Mining Journal* 12.5.1855
49. *Mining Journal* 23.6.1855
50. *Mining Journal* 16.5.1857
51. *Mining Journal* 29.8.1857

Chapter 14

North Ding Dong Mine

The exact location of North Ding Dong Mine is not known; in the *Mining Journal* it was described as "situate immediately east and north of the celebrated Old Ding Dong Mine".[1] The report also states that "The sett is very extensive, and all the standard lodes of the Old Ding Dong pass through it."

This implies that the main workings lay to the east of Ding Dong; presumably part of the sett lay between Ding Dong and East Ding Dong, with the western part of the sett to the north of Ding Dong. Some shafts are shown on the Ordnance Survey maps on Bosporthennis Common, which may relate to this mine. The mine was in 1,024 shares (on which £1 had been paid), the purser was James Permewan (of more later) and managing agent Captain Matthew White, of Marazion; the mine had sold tin when worked seven years prior to this working.[2]

At the end of September 1853 a new lode was intersected in the deep adit level (which had been on the course of the Standard lode, running east-west). The new lode was 12 to 14 inches wide and said to be worth £15 to £20 per fathom.[3] The mine's first accounts are given in the *Cornish Telegraph* in October:[4]

> At the North Ding Dong meeting, on the 21st Sept., the accounts showed - Calls, £1024; chain for East Ding Dong Mine, £10 14s 11d = £1034 14s 11d - By amount of purchase money and the mine cost to March, £512; labour cost for five months to the end of July, £170 19s 5d; smiths' work, £5 2s 10d; merchants' bills, £40 17s 7d; leaving a balance in hand, £305 15s 1d.

In December 1853 the accounts showed a balance in favour of the mine of £132 0s 7d[5] while the accounts to February 1854 gave a positive balance of only £45 2s 5d.[6] No tin had been sold to date and operations were confined to driving the adit north on the new lode; it was expected to cut the north lode by the middle of April.

In August 1854 came the first of many correspondences regarding James Permewan and his somewhat idiosyncratic method of running mines.[7] This was regarding the meeting of shareholders at the East Ding Dong count house on June 23rd; the sender was the enigmatic "R", who had received the information from an impeccable source. The substance of the intelligence was that:

1. No-one had been at the meeting except the purser
2. Resolutions had been passed
3. A call of 10s per share was made
4. A printed statement of accounts was sent to each shareholder, signed by all shareholders present

"R" had also been informed that matters were not in a very satisfactory state at East Ding Dong Mine either, which was under the same management. Not surprisingly, this provoked a response from James Permewan:[8]

NORTH DING DONG MINE,—SIR: I observe in your Journal of the 12th, under the head of Notices to Correspondents, a communication signed "R.," and to satisfy you and the public, I beg to state as follows:—A meeting in the above mine was called on the 23d of June last; three shareholders only resided in Cornwall, one was from home, and another too ill to attend. I was, consequently, the only one present, but I previously consulted the largest holders as to what should be done, and I represented above 300 shares. At the meeting a 10s, call was made; only one absent shareholder objected to it, and he requested a meeting should be called in London; this was done on the 19th July last, when the holders of above 700 (1,024th) shares confirmed the resolution passed at the former meeting, and were satisfied that the 10s. call was proper to be made; and, above this, all present were of the same opinion. But, Sir, with respect to the insinuations regarding my management of East Ding Dong, had "R." one spark of manly feeling about him he would have stated what was unsatisfactory, and likewise put his name to the communication, I would ask him to point me out a mine where more work is done for the money, where the labourers and merchants are more regularly paid, or the accounts kept more straight, and, up to this moment, less fault found by the shareholders against the purser. I am quite aware, Mr, Editor, that although your Journal is open at all times to the public, to express their grievances from the bad management of mines, yet you exercise all due caution to prevent unfounded accusations, which cannot be done in many cases until matters are explained.—JAMES PERMEWAN, Purser of East Ding Dong and North Ding Dong Mines: Aug. 15.

More information regarding the meeting came in a report from Penzance County Court in September, in a the case Hall v Byron.[9] This suit involved an action taken by William Hall, innkeeper, against Robert Byron of London, a Lloyds underwriter for £1 18s 6d, the value of "certain brandy, tobacco, &c., furnished to North Ding Dong Mine". The case had wider implications however, as William Hall had only allowed the suit to be conducted under his name under indemnification, and that the real issue to be tried was whether Byron was owner of 100 shares in the mine, or whether his repudiation of a bargain for that number of shares had been sufficient defence. Hence the case was essentially Permewan v Byron.

When Permewan acquired the sett of North Ding Dong he had proposed to float the mine in 1024 £1 shares. He then went to London in search of shareholders; knowing that Byron was interested in the adjacent mines (*i.e.* he held shares in them) he showed the latter a prospectus and plan and it was agreed to transfer 100 shares to him from John Richards, who held the majority of shares (and had since left the country) The transfer was dated 26th March 1853 and was forwarded to London for Byron's ratification. He held the transfer until April 23rd, when it was returned. In the meantime some correspondence had ensued as the parties in Penzance were keen to complete the list of shareholders. Permewan's solicitor suggested that Byron had been kept back the transfer so that he could watch the share market, "and, if possible, turn his half-completed bargain to advantage".

Permewan was unhappy that the shares could have been sold at a profit but were blocked by Byron; the latter stated that the shares had been offered to him for £30 and had ratified the transfer with this understanding. Permewan denied this and implied a higher price had been offered. Once this demand had been made, Byron repudiated the transaction. This had been understood and acted upon in Penzance, and evidence was given by a young man called Glasson, who, until recently, had been a clerk under Permewan. The latter had contradicted this evidence and the case was the result. During the case, mention was made of the famous meeting attended by Permewan only.

Thus, an enquiry was instituted into the various meetings held in connection with North Ding Dong, and as to how far Mr. Byron had been treated as a shareholder. During the cross-examination of Mr. Permewan, much laughter was caused by the circumstance that a mine meeting had been held, at which resolutions were proposed and carried, nem. con.—that the accounts produced were correct, and showed a balance due to the purser; that a call of 10s. per share should be made; and that the mine's claim on Mr. Byron should be enforced—and a statement was issued, signed by all the adventurers present when, in reality, Mr. Permewan alone attended the meeting. His honour enquired whether the brandy supplied was all consumed it this meeting? while Mr. Pascoe suggested that the toast first following the removal of the cloth must have been "our noble selves."

The case lasted many hours; the judge eventually giving his opinion that the repudiation was sufficient, according to eases recently decided and found for Byron, awarding costs of himself and witness from London.

More information was given the following week in the *Mining Journal*.[10] When Robert Byron was sent was sent his certificates by Permewan, they included the call of £1 per share. Of the total call, £1024, £500 was to go towards the mine and £524 to meet Permewan's advances. Permewan alleged that he had called for a re-transfer to Mr Richards, after which Byron's liabilities would cease, but that Byron refused to transfer his shares or give up his claim on the mine. By doing this, Byron could resume if the mine proved rich, but Permewan refused "so irregular a repudiation".

When Permewan was examined he stated that he had shown Bryon either the original or a copy of the prospectus, and given him in London either a plan or a copy. On his cross-examination, he said that Richards held 800 shares, and Richard Mitchell, of Marazion, 300. The meeting held on the mine on the 23d June had been previously discussed. However, he himself proposed, seconded, and carried unanimously, the resolution that a call of 10s. per share be made. He also moved, seconded, and carried unanimously, the resolutions: That the purser place in the solicitor's hands, without delay, all persons in arrears of calls.

It being represented to the purser that Mr. Byron was likely to give the company some trouble, it was further resolved that the matter be placed in the hands of the company's solicitor. The Judge here asked—"Who drank the gallon of brandy which is amongst the items of Mr. HALL'S account?" Mr. PASCOE, defendant's counsel—"The purser, no doubt, as the representative of other parties, and then proposed the toast, 'Our Noble Selves.'" (Laughter) Permewan had declined to produce his ledger, stating that it had been "surreptitiously carried away" by his clerk.

Robert Byron then wrote to the *Mining Journal* concerning some inaccuracies in its reporting of the case.[11] The first of these was that Permewan's former clerk, R. G. Glasson, was employed by him; this was untrue, and Glasson had no connection with him whatever. Byron also had the opportunity of mentioning some aspects of the trial which had escaped being reported, namely that Permewan had been subpoenaed to produce both the letter book and the share transfer ledger book. In addition, Byron stated that Permewan had denied on oath that he had written letters to John Gilby, of Hull: I have written Mr. Gilby upon the subject of the said letters, and it remains to be seen whether Mr. Permewan shall be proceeded against for having committed the most wilful and gross perjury.

The charges against Permewan's erstwhile clerk he regarded as "void of the slightest foundation"; had Permewan produced the said books they would have "exposed at once and convicted him in the most scandalous and impudent attempt at conspiracy to defraud that can well be imagined".

The same edition of the *Journal* also allowed Permewan to put in a defence of the trial in a long letter, however it was up to Henry English, as editor, to sum this up:

> Mr. PERMEWAN ought to remember that the disclosures respecting the books of the mines, and also respecting the alleged application of the after-acquired shares, do not appear to have received at the trial very satisfactory explanations; and he must himself perceive that his communication has not tended to render these matters more clear, or more creditable.

It was to be four months for the next report of mining, although this merely stated that a valuable lode had been cut.[12] At the end of June more details were given.[13] This stated that the tin had been discovered at the intersection of the Ding Dong Standard Lode with a caunter. The tin ground appeared to improve in depth and was worth at least £50 per fathom. Unfortunately this was to provoke another negative response through the pages of the *Mining Journal*.[14] A month after the report a letter was published stating that the lode in the adit end was very poor, the mine only having produced £12 10s worth of tin for an expenditure of £2,000. The tin found did not exceed £5 per fathom and the materials on the mine worth not more than £30. The letter finished: Really, Mr. Editor, it is painful to contemplate the serious amount of injury that if inflicted upon legitimate mining by such notices, and such conduct ought to be deprecated by every Cornishman. If I am rightly informed, some of the principal shareholders are so dissatisfied with the management and accounts of the mine, that they have not only withdrawn from it, but are taking steps in the Stannaries Court for a full investigation thereof.—Penzance, July 23. Subscriber.

Needless to say, this resulted in a reply,[15] though from Shareholder, not James Permewan, though the style of the letter was very similar to the latter's, something noted in a reply by *Veritas*.[16] "As regards "A Shareholder"," the latter stated, "I think he might, with equal propriety, have signed himself "The Purser;"....". Veritas also asked why the value of actual sales were not given by *A Shareholder*, and not just stating that it was more than £12 10s, speaking from memory.

Two weeks later a report was given of the cause of Provis and others v. Permewan, heard in the Stannaries Court.[17] John Provis, of Warminster, stated that the accounts produced by Permewan the previous May had shown a balance of £189 9s 4d, the allegation against him being that "there were heavy charges in the cost-book which ought not to have been entered therein". Provis wanted the true charges shown to him. The extra costs allegedly included going to London on two occasions to hold meetings there, Permewan's attempts to try to "fix" Robert Byron as a shareholder, and, finally, a large charge to the shareholders for the setts. it was claimed that the mine comprised six setts, from different lords; for three of them, drafts had been drawn but not engrossed (a final copy of the legal contract not having been completed), while for the remainder, no drafts had even been drawn.

Unfortunately the charges for the setts had been allowed at a meeting eighteen months prior to the case, and it seemed there were no circumstances to question the validity of said charges. Following discussion between the Vice-Warden and the advocates, it was decided that the unhappy shareholders could relinquish their shares and give up all claims on the purser and remaining adventurers. James Permewan was to pay £15 costs and "consent to a decree to the above effect whenever required". The outcome of this case also affected those of Minton v. Permewan, and Charlton v. Permewan.

It was a note from "A. Z.", of 164 Fleet Street who provoked the next round of correspondence, after enquiring to purchase 100 shares in the mine.[18] The following week featured a letter from "A Miner" who presumed A. Z. to be James Permewan and implying some nefarious reason for wanting the shares.[19] According to the figures given by *A Miner*:

> Consequently there are only 20 shares held by other persons; but the purser and the public can have no difficulty in supposing who Mr. "A. Z." is; but such scheming and planning should be exposed. I enclose my card.— A MINER: City, Nov. 19.

James Permewan's reply the following week berated Henry English for declining to "furnish me with the name of the foolish and unscrupulous person who strung together the composition signed 'A Miner'".[20] Not only did Permewan deny the information given by *A Miner*, but also attacked the grammar of his letter. In regard to *A Miner's* assertion that only the purser could supply 100 shares, he noted that three gentlemen in Cornwall each held 100 shares over which he had no control; these appear to be the shares recently relinquished by Messrs Byron, Minton and Charlton. Permewan seems to think his reply to *A Miner* one of triumph, as it concludes:

And now, Sir, I have answered *in extenso* every statement, and exposed the insinuations, in the false and discreditable communication of "Miner." His aim may have been to injure the property of the shareholders, or it may amiably have been limited to a desire to malign myself. In both these objects, I wish him joy: I think he has met in each with signal failure. Individually, I could be content to say to him,

"Cease, viper: you bite against a file;" but there are other interests than my own concerned—interests which I am bound to protect, if possible. But I have every right to be well pleased; for I am satisfied and confident that his end will be doubly defeated. Truth will come out of his falsehood, and the public will be enabled to form a higher and juster estimate of the bona fide character of the North Ding Dong Mine. The shareholders, I am sure, will only laugh at "Miner," and thank him for having done them a great, though involuntary, service. Pardon me, Sir, for having occupied so much of your valuable space as I wished to finish "Miner" at one explosion, I could not compress my powder into less compass.

Anderton's Hotel, 164, Fleet-Street, Nov. 28. JAMES PERMEWAN, Purser of North Ding Dong Mine.

In July 1856 William Boyns reported that in driving north on the caunter they had overtaken the tin that had dipped out of the shaft.[21] The lode was 2 feet wide, "and 1 foot of it is nearly solid", which was worth £5 per barrow. The level being driven on the Standard Lode was expected to intersect the Beagle Lode, "where it is believed a good lode will be found". The following month a description of the mine stated that the adit had been driven 300 fathoms to reach the intersection of the Ding Dong Standard Lode and a caunter.[22] Where intersected the lode was found to be good and a shaft had been sunk 40 fathoms; in sinking the shaft a further 6 fathoms some £180 worth of tin had been taken. However, as the tin ground dipped north it was necessary to drive a level to reach it, which had been reported the previous week. In November the report for July 31st stated that the caunter was as good as previously reported, while in driving on the Standard Lode a great improvement was visible. It was expected that a further improvement would take place nearer the intersection with the Beagle Lode.

No further mining reports were made for the mine, which presumably closed in 1857.

References Chapter 14

1. *Mining Journal* 2.8.1856
2. *Mining Journal* 6.7.1853
3. *Mining Journal* 1.10.1853
4. *Cornish Telegraph* 5.10.1853
5. *Mining Journal* 31.12.1853
6. *Mining Journal* 8.4.1854
7. *Mining Journal* 12.8.1854
8. *Mining Journal* 19.8.1854
9. *Mining Journal* 23.9.1854
10. *Mining Journal* 30.9.1854
11. *Mining Journal* 7.10.1854
12. *Mining Journal* 26.2.1855
13. *Mining Journal* 30.6.1855
14. *Mining Journal* 28.7.1855
15. *Mining Journal* 4.8.1855
16. *Mining Journal* 11.8.1855
17. *Mining Journal* 25.8.1855
18. *Mining Journal* 24.11.1855
19. *Mining Journal* 1.12.1855
20. *Mining Journal* 26.7.1856
21. *Mining Journal* 2.8.1856
22. *Mining Journal* 1.11.1856

Chapter 15

Industrial Archaeology

In common with the vast majority of Cornish mines, there is surprisingly little left of the structures built at Ding Dong, in fact in some features have been removed so efficiently that there is only documentary evidence to prove they ever existed. Despite this a number of features can be seen on the mine, most notably the three remaining engine houses.

Engine Houses

Greenburrow

Protection: Listed Grade: II
Date Listed: 18 December 1986
Grid Reference: SW 43448 34423
Engine size: 40 inches
Engine type: Pump
Manufacturer: Harvey & Co.
Condition: Poor, all metal work now corroded and house fenced; remedial work required.

Tredinnick

Protection: Listed Grade: II
Date Listed: 18 December 1986
Grid Reference: SW 4437 3481
Engine size: 30 inches
Engine type: Pump (via flat rods)
Manufacturer: Not known
Condition: poor; removal of vegetation required for proper assessment

Ishmael's Whim

Protection Listed Grade: II
Date Listed 18 December 1986
Grid Reference: SW 4413 3481
Engine size 25 inches
Engine type Whim
Manufacturer Sandys, Vivian & Co.
Condition: comparatively good

Old Greenburrow

Protection: None
Grid Reference: SW 4344 3442
Engine size 30 inches
Engine type: ?Whim
Manufacturer: Not known
Condition: No remains

Old whim

Protection: N/A
Grid Reference: SW 4374 3477
Engine size: 25 inches
Engine type: Whim
Manufacturer: Not known
Condition: No remains seen

Stamps

Protection: N/A
Grid Reference: SW 4374 3472
Engine size: 24 inches
Engine type: Stamps
Manufacturer: Not known
Condition: Unknown, site overgrown

North Killiow

Protection: N/A
Grid Reference: c. SW 4372 3478
Engine size: 40 inches
Engine type: Pump
Manufacturer: Not known
Condition: No remains

Ding Dong

Protection: N/A
Grid Reference: c. SW 4372 3478
Engine size: 30-inches
Engine type: Pump
Manufacturer: Not known
Condition: No remains

South Ding Dong

Protection: N/A
Grid Reference: SW
Engine size: Not known
Engine type: Whim
Manufacturer: Not known
Condition: Unknown, site overgrown

South Ding Dong

Protection: N/A
Grid Reference: SW
Engine size: Not known
Engine type: Whim
Manufacturer: Not known
Condition: No remains

Shafts

Unfortunately it has not been possible to properly reconcile the positions of shafts on the various mine plans with those on the various Ordnance Survey maps. The references below represent, in several instances, a compromise. Some shafts shown on the OS maps are not on the mine plans and *vice versa*.

Name	NGR	Depth	Use	Note	Lode
Bank	43604 34431	70			Malkin
Batten's	43401 34606	40			Bussa
Bolitho's	43500 34586	80			? Wig Lode
Bennet's	43200 34368			1	Green's

Bosilliack		24		1,3	? Bossilliack
Clymo's	43202 34236	20			Good Fortune
Croft Reeve	43754 34754	92			Alex/Clukey/ Malkin Standard
Davey's	43355 34580				Bussa
Ding Dong	43802 34774	100	P	2	Ding Dong Standard
East	43374 34333				not known
East Killiow		24			? Providence
Engine	43802 34774		W	3	Ding Dong Standard
Flat Rod	44182 34876			5	not known
Good Fortune				3	White
Graham's				3	not known
Greenburrow	43446 34428	104	W/P		Malkin
Greenpease	43698 34508	60			Malkin
Hard	43975 34834	62			Ding Dong Standard
Highburrow	43557 34688	18			Sut Bal
Ishmael's	44040 34868	62	W		not known
Jacobine	43713 34616	50			Jacobine
Killiow				6	After's
Killiow Engine	43802 34774		P		Ding Dong Standard
New Flat-rod			W	3	not known
North Killiow	43802 34774	100			Ding Dong Standard
Old Engine	43512 34420	24	P		Good Fortune
Providence	44128 34856	110	P		Qualk
Qualk	44096 34750	55		2	not known
Quoil	44078 34936			7	not known
Robin's	43879 34976	80			Robin's
South Bussa	43421 34519	30			Bussa
South Killiow	43950 34596	59			? Providence
Tallow		>50		3	Tallow/Bucka

Notes

1. Bennet's Shaft may be Bosilliack Shaft

2. Engine Shaft probably North Killiow/Killiow Engine Shaft
3. These shafts not located
4. Possibly Old Flat Rod Shaft
5. Possibly also called Trathan's Shaft
6. Probably North Killiow/Ding Dong Shaft
7. Only on OS map

Other features (from east to west)

Count house (private property)	SW 4422 3478
Tramway	SW 4395 3483
Pond for Killiow engine (presumed)	SW 4383 3482
Pond for old whim engine (presumed)	SW 4373 3476
Site of dry	SW 4369 3475
Dressing floors (centre)	SW 4375 3470
Reservoir for dressing floors	SW 4365 3467
Reservoir for dressing floors	SW 4369 3465
Reservoir for dressing floors	SW 4373 3464
Pond for Greenburrow engine house	SW 4351 3447
Greenburrow shaft capstan	SW 4344 3442

Index

215